16-99

PC Operation and Repair

K.F. Ibrahim
Senior Lecturer
College of North West London

 Longman

Pearson Education Limited
Edinburgh Gate
Harlow, Essex CM20 2JE, England
and Associated Companies throughout the world.

Published in the United States of America
by Addison Wesley Longman Publishing, New York

© Addison Wesley Longman Limited 1998

First published 1998
Third impression 2000

ISBN 0-582-30582-9

British Library Cataloguing-in-Publication Data

A catalogue record for this book is
available from the British Library

Set by 4 in 10/12pt Times
Printed in Malaysia, PP

Contents

Preface

PC Operation and Repair is a textbook which takes the reader from the basics of microprocessor systems to advanced installation and configuration of personal computers in easy logical steps through which concepts and techniques are explained. The book does not presume advanced knowledge of microprocessors or computers by the reader. All that is required is enthusiasm for the subject and a knowledge of basic concepts of physics and mathematics. Throughout the book, I have attempted to include the latest computer techniques.

The book covers all aspects of a personal computer, its operation, configuration and installation. It ends with a chapter on fault finding which breaks away from the static approach, flowchart-based fault finding, and introduces a logical deductive approach to fault diagnosis. My approach relies on sound knowledge of the system, the processes involved in the operation of a PC and its peripherals.

A number of appendices are included which provide useful references to instruments and testing, binary and hexadecimal numbers, MS DOS commands, logic devices and chip markings.

The book is suitable for students taking City and Guilds PC Installation and Repair modules 324 (level 2) and 344 (level 3) of the IT series 7261 as well as other modules such as 226 (DOS) and 227 (data communication and networking). It is also suitable for students, and others, who wish to acquaint themselves with computer hardware, operation, upgrading, maintenance and repair. Computer enthusiasts will find the book a useful tool.

As an aid to revision and self-testing, two separate sets of multiple choice questions are included in Appendix 6. Thirty questions for the intermediate level (C & G 324) and 65 questions for the advanced level (C & G 344) are provided together with answers.

In writing this book, it was my intention to provide a worthy alternative to the grossly inflated, highly verbose publications that came to life as aggregated articles and which have saturated the PC book market world-wide. In this endeavour, I trust I have succeeded.

K. F. IBRAHIM
NOVEMBER 1997

1 Microprocessor fundamentals

The development of the personal computer followed closely upon the development of integrated circuits. The introduction of very large and ultra large scale integration (VLSI and ULSI) which contain the equivalent of a million or more transistors paved the way for the manufacture of complex circuits and complete systems on a single silicon chip. Three main technologies are employed in the fabrication of integrated circuits: TTL, CMOS and NMOS.

TTL (Transistor–Transistor Logic) is fast, consumes more power compared with the other two types and has a low package density. CMOS (Complementary Metal Oxide Silicon) is slower than TTL. However, its power requirement is very low and its package density is much higher than the TTL type, i.e. it can pack more electronic elements such as transistors into a square millimetre of a silicon chip. NMOS (N-channel MOS) is far less complex than CMOS and as such has greater package density. However, its power requirements are greater than CMOS. Where power requirements are not a problem, NMOS technology is normally used for the processor, other support chips and most of the memory chips.

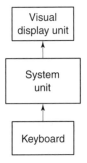

Figure 1.1 Essential elements of a personal computer

The PC – an overview

The very first personal computer (PC) was the **XT** (eXtended Technology). It was launched by IBM on 12 August 1981. This was followed a few years later by the **AT** (Advanced Technology) type using the 80286, 80386, 80486 and the current Pentium processors.

Although a computer system may have several external devices connected to it, such as a printer, a mouse and a digitiser, the essential elements of personal computers are the same, namely a system unit, a keyboard and a visual display unit (VDU) or monitor (Fig. 1.1). The keyboard provides the user with access to the system unit while the monitor provides a visual display of the textual output of the keyboard as well as information and messages from the system unit.

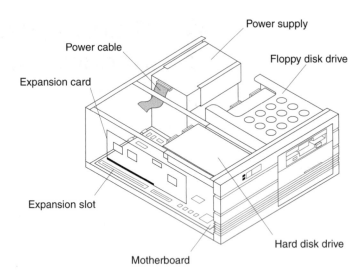

Figure 1.2 The system unit

The system unit

The system unit contains all the devices and circuitry necessary for the operation of the computer. The component parts of a system unit (Fig. 1.2) are:

    The power supply
    Disk drives
    Expansion or adaptor cards
    The motherboard
    Connectors or ports which provide access to external devices (printer, mouse, VDU, modem, etc.)

The power supply

The power supply converts a.c. mains into the necessary stabilised d.c. voltages for the motherboard, the keyboard and other elements within the system unit including the expansion cards. The power supply provides +5 V, −5 V, +12 V and −12 V together with a power good (PG) signal for the processor.

Disk drives

Disk drives are mass data storage devices. A typical computer employs two types of disk drives: a floppy and a hard disk drive. Data is stored on concentric tracks that have been formatted onto a plastic (floppy) or metal (hard) disk which has been coated with a very thin layer of electromagnetic material. The disk drives are connected either directly to the motherboard or via an adaptor card using multi-line flat ribbon cables.

Expansion (adaptor) cards

Expansion or adaptor cards are printed circuit boards which support essential elements such as disk drives and video displays or add-on facilities such as CD-ROMs and modems by simply inserting them into expansion slots on the motherboard.

The motherboard

The motherboard, also known as the system board, is the core of the computer system. It contains all the necessary components (including the processor and other support and logic chips) and circuitry for the operation of the system. A motherboard is known by the type of processor it supports – hence a 386 (using an 80386 processor), a 486 or a Pentium motherboard. Modern motherboards are designed to support more than one type of processor, making it possible to upgrade the system without changing the motherboard. The components of a typical motherboard (Fig. 1.3) are:

A *central processing unit* (CPU) together with a number of supporting chips to assist the processor in its task of controlling the operation and timing of all units and devices.

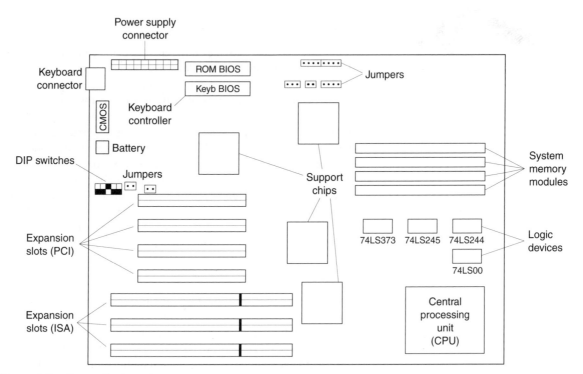

Figure 1.3   The motherboard

Memory chips or modules which provide an on-board store known as system memory. This memory store is far smaller than the storage capacity of the disk drives. However, it is more than 1000 times faster.

Logic devices to perform a variety of essential functions such as:

- simple gate, e.g. the 7400 (quad two-input NAND) and the 7404 (octal inverters);
- buffers which isolate one stage from another preventing overloading, e.g. the 7408;
- multiplexers which enable two or more signals to use a single line by rapid switching from one signal to the next.

Programmed memory chips which hold a permanent program or a conversion table such as the keyboard controller and the basic input/output system (BIOS) chips.

Expansion slots also known as expansion buses which allow adaptor cards to be plugged into the motherboard to perform additional functions to those performed by the motherboard.

A *keyboard connector* to plug in the keyboard cable.

A *power connector* for d.c. power from the power supply.

Jumpers for configuring the system to the required specifications.

Connectors and ports

A computer system provides a number of connectors and ports for communication with the outside world. Some of these connectors, such the keyboard connector, are available directly from the motherboard; others are provided by adaptor cards such as input/output ports. Connectors may be identified by their shape and pin numbers as shown in Table 1.1. Two types of input/output (I/O) ports are provided, the parallel and serial. In the parallel mode, the component parts of the digital information, i.e the binary bits, are transmitted simultaneously on several lines, while in the serial mode they are transmitted one after the other on a single line. A PC supports up to four serial ports known as COM1, COM2, COM3 and COM4 and up to three parallel ports known as LPT1, LPT2 and LPT3. There is also a video port which connects the computer to the display unit.

Digital information Digital information takes the form of bits (binary digits). A single bit can have one of two states: a zero or LOW and a one or HIGH. The amount of information that can be exchanged using 1 bit only is very limited (ON or OFF, YES or NO, 0 or 1). Using 2 bits, the amount of information is doubled. Four different combinations ($2^2 = 4$) may be obtained with 2 bits as shown in Table 1.2.

Table 1.1

Connector shape	Application
25-way 'D'	Male type: serial (RS232) COM 1, COM 2, COM 3, COM 4 Female type: parallel (Centronics) LPT1, LPT2, LPT3
9-way 'D'	Male type: (a) serial (RS232) COM 1, COM 2, COM 3, COM 4 (b) mouse Female type: video (mono, CGA, EGA)
15-way 'D' (3 rows)	Female type only: (a) video (VGA, SVGA) (b) network
15-way 'D' (two rows)	Female type only: games port
5-way or 6-way DIN	Keyboard
BNC	Network

Table 1.2 Different combinations with 2 bits

Bit 1	Bit 0
0	0
0	1
1	0
1	1

Table 1.3 Different combinations with 3 bits

b2	b1	b0
0	0	0
0	0	1
0	1	0
0	1	1
1	0	0
1	0	1
1	1	0
1	1	1

Using 3 bits doubles the quantity of information yet again with $2^3 = 8$ different combinations (Table 1.3) and so on. A digital package of information consists of a number of bits grouped together to form a word, which is the basic unit of information, e.g. an 8-bit word or a 16-bit word. A word can only make sense when all the bits have been received. The bits may be sent one at a time along a single line, a method known as serial transmission (Fig. 1.4a). Alternatively, the bits may be transmitted simultaneously, i.e. in parallel (Fig. 1.4b).

The CPU employs the parallel mode to communicate with the various units in the system using a standard word length of 16 bits. The parallel lines carrying the multi-bit digital information form what is known as a bus.

Each logic level is represented by a voltage level. For TTL technology, a logic HIGH is represented by a high voltage between 2.8 to 5 V and a logic LOW is represented by a low voltage (0 to 0.4 V).

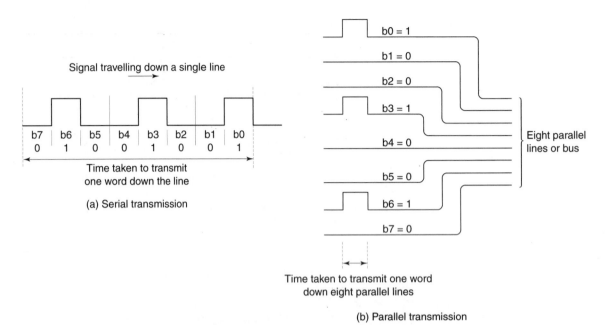

Figure 1.4 Serial and parallel transmission

Microprocessor system basic architecture

The basic architecture of a microprocessor computer system is shown in Fig. 1.5. It consists of the following components parts:

The central processing unit (CPU)
Memory chips; RAM and ROM
An address decoder chip
Input and output interface chips; PIO and UART
A direct memory access controller (DMAC)
A programmable interrupt controller (PIC)
A bus structure

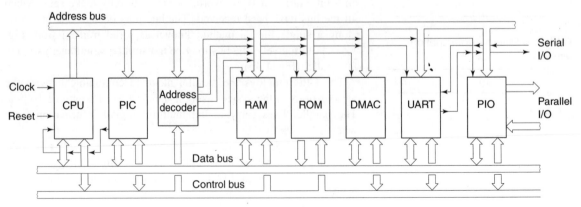

Figure 1.5 Microprocessor computer architecture

The CPU

The CPU is usually a single VLSI device chip containing all the necessary circuitry to interpret and execute program instructions in terms of data manipulation, logic and arithmetic operations and timing and control of the system. The capacity or size of a microprocessor chip is determined by the number of data bits it can handle. A 4-bit processor has a 4-bit data width and an 8-bit chip has an 8-bit data width and so on. The smaller 4-bit and 8-bit processors are generally employed as dedicated controllers in industrial applications and domestic appliances such as washing machines and TV receivers.

Modern PCs use 32-bit processors such as the 486 and the Pentium. Early generation computers used the 16-bit 80286 and, earlier still, the XT computer used the 8-bit 8088 processor. Microprocessors also differ in the speed with which they execute instructions. CPU speed is indicated by the frequency of the system clock in megahertz (MHz, millions of cycles per second). While the bit width or size determines the quantity of information that may be transferred in any one cycle, the speed determines the number of such transactions per second.

Table 1.4 lists the CPUs in common use by PC manufacturers, the year they were launched, their bit size and speed.

Table 1.4

CPU	Launched	Bit size	Speed (MHz)
8088	1979	8	5
8086	1978	16	8
80286	1982	16	8 – 12
80386	1985	32	16 – 25
80486	1989	32	25 – 100
Pentium	1993	32	60 – 200

CPU control signals

The number and type of control signals depends on the microprocessor used and the design of the system. Control signals are normally active low, i.e. active when at logic 0. Active low signals are signified by a bar ($^-$). The main control signals of a CPU are as follows.

The clock pulse signal

Figure 1.6 The clock pulse waveform

A clock pulse (Fig. 1.6) is an essential requirement for the operation of the processor. The clock control signal synchronises the movement of the data around the various elements of the system

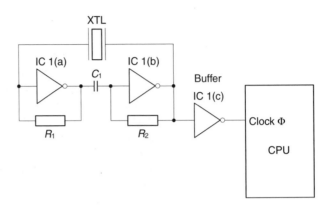

Figure 1.7 Crystal-controlled clock oscillator

and determines the speed of operation, without which the system comes to a halt. A crystal-controlled oscillator is used to provide accurate and stable timing clock pulses as shown in Fig. 1.7. Clock frequencies vary from 8 MHz in the relatively slow 80286 processor to the faster 80486 and Pentium chips of 150 MHz and over.

Read (RD) and write (WR)

The CPU determines the direction of data transfer to or from the microprocessor chip. This is carried out by the read and write control lines. In a READ operation when the CPU is receiving data from memory, the READ line is active allowing data to be transferred to the CPU. In a WRITE operation when the CPU is sending data to memory, the WRITE line is active enabling data transfer from the CPU to memory.

Interrupts

When a peripheral device such as a printer, a keyboard or a modem needs attention, a hardware interrupt signal, INTR (interrupt request), is sent to the CPU. When such a signal is received, the main program is interrupted temporarily to allow the CPU to deal with the request. After servicing the peripheral device, the CPU returns to the original program at the point where it left it. INTR is one type of hardware interrupt where the CPU will complete the current instruction that is being executed before recognising the interrupt. Other interrupts such as HALT stop the execution of the main program to allow an external source or device to execute a different program.

Reset ($\overline{RES}$ or $\overline{REST}$)

This is a type of interrupt which overrides all other interrupts and inputs. The reset input pin is normally held HIGH. If it is taken LOW by a manual reset or by an accident or fault, it immediately

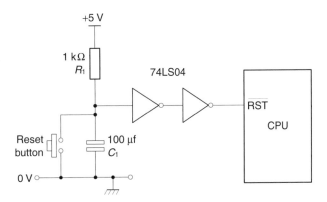

Figure 1.8 Simple R-C reset circuit

stops the CPU program, and the processor is reset. To restart the microprocessor operations, the reset pin must be taken HIGH again.

Fig. 1.8 shows a press button manual reset circuit. When power is switched on, and 5 V d.c. supply is established, capacitor C_1 charges up through the 1k resistor. After a short time determined by time constant C_1R_1 (0.1 s), the reset pin goes to logic HIGH. When that happens, the microprocessor immediately commences an initialisation sequence. This sequence consists of directing the CPU to the memory location where the start-up program of the system is stored. The reset pin is held at logic high via the 1k resistor. Two TTL low power Schottky (LS) inverters/buffers (74LS04) are used to ensure that the correct logic levels are established.

The system may be reset by switching the power off and then on. This is known as a 'cold' start. A 'warm' start may be executed by the use of a reset push button (Fig. 1.8). When the press button is pressed, the switch closes and capacitor C_1 is discharged taking the reset pin to logic 0 (LOW). All operations are suspended. If the press button is then released, C_1 charges up through resistor R_1 taking the reset pin back to logic 1.

The memory store

A memory store consists of a number of memory locations where data in the form of digital bits is stored. Each location stores 8 bits of data known as a byte. Each location is given a unique binary address. The number of addressable locations is determined by the number of bits in an address. An address with 3 bits (A0, A1 and A2) provides a maximum of $2^3 = 8$ memory locations. Alternatively, a 10-bit (A0–A9) address has $2^{10} = 1024$ or 1k memory locations (Fig. 1.9). The address lines are grouped together to form an address bus. By placing an address on the address bus, any one of the 1024 locations may be selected. For instance, if A9, A8, ..., A1, A0 are set to logic levels 0, 0, 1, 0, 1, 1, 0, 1, 0, 1, then the location with

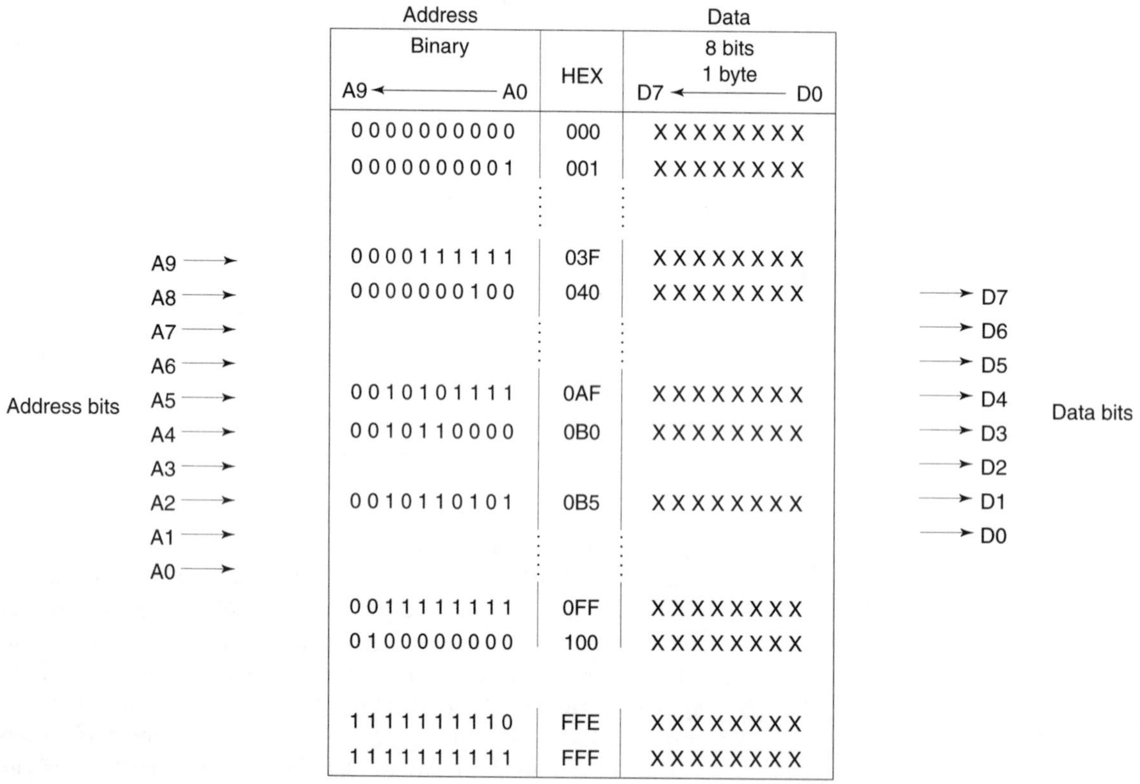

Address			Data		
Binary		HEX	8 bits 1 byte		
A9 ◄———————— A0			D7 ◄———————— D0		
0 0 0 0 0 0 0 0 0 0		000	X X X X X X X X		
0 0 0 0 0 0 0 0 0 1		001	X X X X X X X X		
⋮		⋮	⋮		
0 0 0 0 1 1 1 1 1 1		03F	X X X X X X X X		
0 0 0 0 0 0 0 1 0 0		040	X X X X X X X X		
⋮		⋮			
0 0 1 0 1 0 1 1 1 1		0AF	X X X X X X X X		
0 0 1 0 1 1 0 0 0 0		0B0	X X X X X X X X		
0 0 1 0 1 1 0 1 0 1		0B5	X X X X X X X X		
⋮		⋮			
0 0 1 1 1 1 1 1 1 1		0FF	X X X X X X X X		
0 1 0 0 0 0 0 0 0 0		100	X X X X X X X X		
⋮		⋮			
1 1 1 1 1 1 1 1 1 0		FFE	X X X X X X X X		
1 1 1 1 1 1 1 1 1 1		FFF	X X X X X X X X		

Address bits
A9 →
A8 →
A7 →
A6 →
A5 →
A4 →
A3 →
A2 →
A1 →
A0 →

Data bits
→ D7
→ D6
→ D5
→ D4
→ D3
→ D2
→ D1
→ D0

Figure 1.9 Basic memory organisation

address 0010110101 in binary (0B5 in hexadecimal) is selected. For simplicity, addresses are normally stated in hexadecimal. Once a memory location is chosen, pins D0 to D7 on the chip provide access to the eight memory cells in that location. Lines D0, D1, D2, ..., D7 are grouped together to form a data bus to carry the data bits.

One of the more important specifications of a CPU is the number of address pins provided. This determines the maximum number of addressable memory locations that the system can accommodate. For instance, the 8088/86 with 20 address lines (A0–A19) provide a total number of memory locations of

$$2^{20} = 2^{10} \times 2^{10} = 1k \times 1k = 1 \text{ million locations or } 1M$$

The address range extends from 00000 (HEX) to FFFFF (HEX). With each location holding an 8-bit (1-byte) word, the total memory is therefore 1 megabyte or 1MB.

The 80286 with 24 address lines provides 16MB of memory while the 80386, 80486 and the Pentium have 32 address lines for a total memory of 4000MB or 4 gigabytes (4GB).

The memory store shown in Fig. 1.5 consists of two types of

chips: RAM (Random Access Memory) and ROM (Read Only Memory). RAM is a volatile momory, i.e. a memory that loses its contents when power is switched off, which the CPU may read from and write to. ROM is a non-volatile memory which is used for permanent storage of programs or data. Computers usually use other types of memory such as non-volatile RAM (NV-RAM), Programmable ROM (PROM), which are blank ROMs that can be programmed once only, and the Erasable PROM (EPROM) which may be programmed several times.

Each memory chip occupies a block within the total available memory. A location is selected by placing an address on the address bus. The memory chip which contains the selected location is enabled by the address decoder, which monitors the state of the higher address lines and selects the appropriate chip by taking its chip select (CS) pin LOW.

The input/output (I/O) interface

The input/output interface unit connects the system to external devices. It acts as an input or an output route for transferring data to and from the peripheral devices such as a printer, a display unit, a modem or a mouse. Two types of I/O devices are shown in Fig. 1.5: PIO and UART. The PIO (Parallel Input/Output) also known as the PIA (Parallel Interface Adaptor), provides a parallel communication path to and from the system. The PIO is mainly used for printer operation. The UART (Universal Asynchronous Receiver/ Transmitter) provides a serial communication route with external devices such as modems and mice.

The I/O interface chips are programmable, i.e. they may be used to serve devices with different specifications. A programmable I/O chip has a number of internal registers. A register is a small memory store, normally 8 bits in length. The mode of operation of the I/O chip is defined by the contents of these registers which may be altered by the CPU. When an external device such as a modem requests attention, the CPU first initialises the I/O interface, in this case the UART, by loading the appropriate codes in its registers for the specific requirements of the modem such as speed and bit length. When the UART is initialised, the CPU then calls a program known as a service routine which allows the system to communicate with the modem.

Direct memory access controller (DMAC)

The vast majority of computer operations involve the transfer of data between different units of the system. This is normally carried out by the processor itself. Where a large amount of data is to be

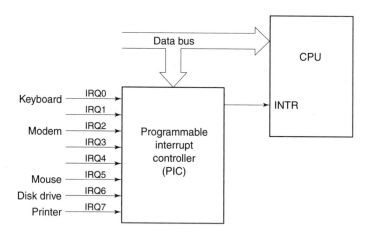

Figure 1.10 The programmable interrupt controller

transferred, a faster method, known as direct memory access (DMA), is normally used in which a controller, DMAC, takes control of the system for the duration of the transfer. Once the data transfer has been completed, the DMAC hands control back to the CPU.

Programmable interrupt controller (PIC)

Normally more than one external peripheral device has to share a single INTR pin on the processor. Each peripheral device generates an interrupt request (IRQ) signal which is sent to a PIC as shown in Fig. 1.10. The PIC determines the order in which the various IRQs are dealt with by the CPU.

The bus structure

The hardware elements described above are interconnected with each other by a bus structure consisting of three types of buses: address, data and control, as shown in Fig. 1.5. The address and data buses provide a parallel highway along which multi-bit addresses and data travel from one unit to another. The control bus incorporates the lines that carry the control signals to and from the CPU.

General operation of the system

The heart of the system, the microprocessor, operates on a *fetch and execute* cycle. During the fetch phase, the CPU retrieves an instruction from the memory location where the program is stored. The fetch is achieved by the microprocessor placing the address of the appropriate memory location on the address bus and enabling the

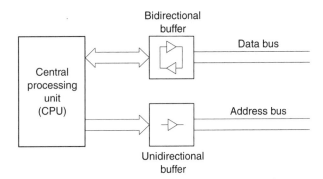

Figure 1.11 Address and data buffers

READ control line. The address decoder will select the appropriate memory chip which places the contents of that location, i.e. the instruction, in the form of a coded binary word on the data bus. The CPU receives the instruction and stores it in an internal register known as the instruction register. During the execute phase, the CPU having received the instruction, decodes it and proceeds to execute it. This is carried out by the CPU generating the necessary timing and control signals for the execution of that particular instruction. The execute phase may involve simple arithmetic operations, e.g. addition or subtraction, or more complex data transfer to or from memory or peripheral devices. Both the fetch and execute phases may take more than one clock cycle to complete depending on the nature of the instruction. When the instruction is completed, the microprocessor then places the next program address, i.e. the address where the next instruction is stored, on the address bus commencing another fetch and execute cycle and so on.

Bus buffers

The bus connects the microprocessor to all memory and interface devices in the system. However, microprocessors of the MOS type lack the drive needed for a large system. For this reason, bus drivers or buffers are used to boost the driving capability of the buses.

There are two types of drivers: a transmitter for driving the bus and a receiver for listening to the bus. In bidirectional buses such as the data bus, a transmitter/receiver is employed, known as a bidirectional buffer or transceiver as shown in Fig. 1.11. Tristate buffers may also be employed to disconnect the bus from the microprocessor. This technique is used when an external device takes control of the system from the CPU.

2 An introduction to MS-DOS commands

PC hierarchy

A computer is a combination of hardware (i.e. the actual physical units, components and circuitry that make up the system) and software (i.e. the coded instructions and programs). The highest level of software is the application package such as word processing, spreadsheet or games software (Fig. 2.1). An application package is a program or a set of programs which can only be used in the environment for which it was designed to run. Such an environment is known as the operating system. The operating system is itself a collection of programs or routines that are called upon by the application program as and when necessary. There are several operating systems, the most popular of which are MS-DOS (Microsoft Disk Operating System) and Windows. Others include OS/2 and UNIX.

PCs are general purpose systems that are designed to accommodate different operating systems. The link between the hardware and a specific operating system is a set of software routines known as BIOS (Basic Input/Output System). BIOS provides for the software to take control of the hardware at a very basic and fundamental level. Its program routines are permanently stored in a ROM or a PROM chip. Because of their permanent nature, BIOS routines are referred to as firmware.

Where a graphical user interface (GUI) is used, such as Windows' icons, a further level of software is introduced between the application programs and the operating system in the PC hierarchy shown in Fig. 2.1.

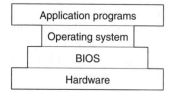

Figure 2.1 Hardware/software hierarchy

DOS versions

Since its release in 1981, DOS has been updated to accommodate developments in hardware and software and the ever expanding needs of the user. Each new release was identified by a number, 1, 2, 3 and so on. Within each major version, a number of updates were introduced and these were identified with a decimal number – hence the 5.0 and 6.2 versions.

There are a number of ways of identifying the version of DOS that is being used by a computer. The simplest way is to use one of DOS's own commands available in versions 4.0 onwards, namely VER.

Internal and external commands

Operating system MS-DOS is a set of program routines. All such routines are stored on the hard disk under appropriate filenames, e.g. COPY or DELETE. A command is excuted by simply typing the keyword which represents the command at the prompter (e.g. DIR for directory listing) and pressing the return key. When the return key is pressed, the CPU goes to the hard disk and searches for the file containing the particular command routine and executes it. Reading files from the hard disk takes a relatively long time. A much faster method is to store the command files in the system memory itself. However, this will require a large chunk of very precious memory to be devoted entirely to a list of files some of which may be used very infrequently, if at all. For this reason, commands are divided into two categories: internal or residential and external or non-residential.

Internal commands are those commands which are frequently used, such as directory (DIR), copy (COPY), delete (DEL) and clear screen (CLS). The files relating to these commands are copied into the system memory at the booting up stage of the computer, i.e. when it is switched on.

External commands are non-essential commands which are not regularly required. Such commands include FORMAT, PRINT and DISKCOPY. These command files remain on the hard disk and are transferred to the system memory only when required. Once transferred, they remain in the system memory until the PC is switched off or rebooted.

File management

DOS treats a file simply as a collection of information to be stored and retrieved as a unit. To distinguish one file from another, the file is given a name. This name is made up of two parts separated by a dot (.). The first part is called the filename and the second part is called the extension. The filename can have up to eight characters. The extension is optional and can have up to three characters which are usually used to signify the type of information the file contains, for instance ABC.TXT for a text file called ABC, IO.SYS for a system file called IO, and WP51.BAT for a batch file called WP51. When calling a file, the full name, i.e. the filename and the extension, must be specified. Spaces and some keyboard characters, e.g. *, ?, \, /, ", :, < and >, are not acceptable as filenames.

Drives and directories

The hard and floppy disks are the usual places where files are stored. Each disk drive is identified by a letter followed by a colon, e.g. A:

(drive A) and C: (drive C). Letters A and B are reserved for floppy drives and C onwards are used for hard disk drives. A computer with one hard drive and one floppy drive will therefore have drives C: and A: respectively. Drives are divided into directories where files may be saved. Each directory may be divided into a number of subdirectories and so on. The main directory is referred to as the root directory.

Before a file may be called, its directory and subdirectory must be identified. This is known as the file *path*. For instance, a file called ADDRESS.LBL saved in directory WP51 which is a subdirectory of root directory C:\ has the following file path specification:

C:\WP51\ADDRESS.LBL

The DOS prompt

When the operating system is loaded, a prompt appears on the screen. The usual DOS prompt indicates the current drive and the directory or subdirectory if appropriate, e.g.

C:\> (drive C:, root directory) or
A:\WINDOWS\> (drive A:, subdirectory WINDOWS)

Some DOS commands

DOS has a large number of commands that are available for use at the prompt. The number of these commands has increased with each version of DOS. The following commands are based on versions 5.0 and above (a list of DOS commands is given in Appendix 1).

TASK	**To change the drive**
FORM	**C:\>D:**
Comments	where D is the new drive
Example	C:\>A: *to change to drive A: (in which case a new prompt will be displayed, A:\>)*

TASK	**Directory listing (to list files in a directory)**
FORM	**C:\>DIR D:** or **DIR D:**
Comments	where DIR is the command, D the drive and \ the root
Example	C:\>DIR C: *(to list files in root directory C:)*

TASK	**To list files contained in a subdirectory**
FORM	**C:\>DIR D:\subdirectory**
Example	C:\>DIR C:\DOS *(to list files in a subdirectory called DOS)*

TASK	**Directory listing – wide format**
FORM	**C:\>DIR D:/w**
Comments	where / is a switch and w represents wide
Example	C:\>DIR A:/w

TASK	**Directory listing – page by page**
FORM	**C:\>DIR D:/p**
Example	C:\>DIR C:\DOS/p

TASK	**Change directory**
FORM	**C:\>CD subdirectory**
Example	C:\>CD DOS *(when this command is executed the following prompt should be displayed: C:\DOS\>)*

TASK	**To return to root directory**
FORM	**C:\>CD ..**
Example	C:\DOS> CD.. *(after execution, the following will be displayed C:\>)*

TASK	**To make a new directory**
FORM	**C:\>MD newdirectory**
Example	C:\>MD FOOTBALL

TASK	**To view the directory/subdirectory structure**
FORM	**C:\>TREE D:**
Examples	C:\>TREE C: *to display the directory structure of root directory C:* C:\>TREE C:/f *to list the names of files as well* C:\>TREE C:/f |MORE *to show the structure and files page by page*

TASK	**To copy a file**
FORM	**C:\>COPY D:\filename.ext E:**
Comments	where D:\filename.ext is the source and E: the destination drive
Examples	C:\>COPY C:\AUTOEXEC.BAT A: C:\>COPY A:\FOOTBALL\PREMIER.96 C:

TASK	**The use of wild card copy**
FORM	**C:\>COPY D:\filename.* E:**
Comments	where filename.* is the source regardless of the file extension
Examples	C:\>COPY C:\FOOTBALL.* A: C:\>COPY A:*.* C: *(copies all files in A: to C:)* C:\>COPY A:*.* C:\FOOTBALL *(where C:\FOOTBALL is the destination subdirectory)*

TASK	**To copy a file to a different drive and name**
FORM	**C:\>COPY D:\filename.ext E:\newname.ext**
Comments	where E:\newname.ext is the destination new filename
Example	C:\>COPY C:\AUTOEXEC.BAT A:AUTO.BAK

TASK	**To copy from a subdirectory**
FORM	**C:\>COPY D:\subdirectory\filename.ext E:**
TASK	**To copy from one subdirectory to another**
FORM	**C:\>COPY D:\subdirectory\filename.ext E: \subdirectory**
TASK	**To move files**
FORM	**C:\>MOVE D:\filename.ext E:**
Example	C:\>MOVE A:LETTER.OL C:\
TASK	**To erase or delete files**
FORM	**C:\>DEL D:\filename.ext**
Example	C:\>DEL A:\AUTO.BAK
TASK	**To remove a directory (the directory must be empty)**
FORM	**C:\>RD D:\subdirectory**
Example	C:\>RD C:\FOOTBALL
TASK	**To rename a file**
FORM	**C:\>REN D:\OLDNAME.TX1 D:\NEWNAME.TX2**
Example	C:\> REN C:\AUTOEXEC.BAT C:\AUTOEXEC.NEW
TASK	**To duplicate a disk**
FORM	**C:\>DISKCOPY D: E:**
Comments	where D is the source disk drive and E the destination drive
Examples	C:\>DISKCOPY A: B: *to duplicate source disk 1 in drive A: on target disk 2 in drive B:*
	C: >DISKCOPY A: A: *to duplicate source disk 1 in drive A: to target disk 2 which replaces disk 1 when prompted by the system*

Attributes

Files may be given certain attributes which could for instance provide protection from deletion or being overwritten, or hide a file from being displayed by the DIR command.

Files may be assigned one or more of the following attributes:

R   Read only to protect a file from change.
S   System file.
H   Hidden to keep a file away from directory listing.
A   Archive to indicate whether a file has been changed since it was backed up to another disk.

TASK	**To list the attributes of all files in a directory**
FORM	**C:\>ATTRIB D:**
Example	C:\>ATTRIB C: *to show the attributes of all files including any hidden files in root directory C:*

TASK	**To assign an attribute to a file**
FORM	**C:\>ATTRIB +attribute D:\filename**
Example	C:\>ATTRIB +R C:\COMMAND.COM *to make COMMAND.COM a read only file*

TASK	**To remove an attribute from a file**
FORM	**C:\>ATTRIB -attribute D:\filename**
Example	C:\>ATTRIB -H C:\IO.SYS *to allow IO.SYS to be shown in a directory listing*

TYPE Command

The contents of a file may be displayed on the screen by the TYPE command.

FORM	**C:\>TYPE D:\filename**
Example	C:\>TYPE C:\AUTOEXEC.BAT

MODE Command

The MODE command covers a multitude of functions. The following are some of the commonly used functions:

TASK	**To set the number of characters on the screen**
FORM	**C:\>MODE CON COLS=n**
	or simply
	MODE n
Comments	where n is the number of characters per line
Example	C:\>MODE 40 *for 40 characters*

TASK	**To set the number of lines on the screen**
FORM	**C:\>MODE CON LINES=n**
Comments	where n may be 25, 43 or 50

TASK	**To redirect output to printer from parallel to serial**
FORM	**C:\>MODE LPTx=COMy**
Comments	where x and y are the numbers of the parallel and serial ports respectively
Example	C:\>MODE LPT1=COM2 *to redirect output to printer from parallel port LPT1 to serial port COM2*

TASK	**To display the status of devices installed on the computer.**
FORM	**C:\\>MODE**

The MODE command may also be used to configure a printer and a serial port.

Batch files A batch file is a file containing a sequence of command lines which will be executed by the computer, line by line, when the file is called. A batch file always has the extension .BAT. operating system MS-DOS has an editor which allows the user to create or change the contents of a file. The editor mode is entered by the EDIT command. For instance, to create or amend a batch file called AUTOEXEC.BAT, type the following at the DOS prompt:

EDIT AUTOEXEC.BAT

Once the editor mode is entered, writing a batch file is a simple matter of typing the command lines in the desired sequence. While any DOS command may be used in a batch file, the following are some of the commands that are dedicated for batch files:

ECHO ON	to display command lines on the screen as they are executed
ECHO OFF	to turn off the screen display of command lines
ECHO	to display a message on the screen
PAUSE	suspends the processing of a batch program and displays the following message: 'press any key to continue'
REM	appears at the start of a line to make it ineffective; it therefore enables remarks to be included or prevents the execution of a command without removing it from the file.

3 The power supply

All electronic equipment requires direct current and voltages for its operation. Portable equipment such as radio cassette recorders or laptop computers employ a battery for this purpose. Other equipment such as a television receiver or a desktop computer plugs directly into the mains electrical power. If this is of the alternating current (a.c.) type, it has to be converted into direct current (d.c.) before it can be used to drive the electronic circuitry. Such a converter is known as the power supply.

The PC power supply unit

The power supply unit is a self-contained sealed unit which houses all the high voltage circuitry. The metal container prevents high frequency interference which could cause havoc with digital systems. It is cooled by an electric fan which, in addition to extracting air from the unit, helps to cool the motherboard and other devices and cards inside the unit. The flow of air also prevents dust from settling on chips and other electronic components. The noise that is heard when a computer is turned on is that of the cooling fan.

d.c. requirements of a PC

A computer system requires a number of stabilised d.c. voltages to drive the motherboard and other peripheral devices and adaptor cards. Table 3.1 lists the voltage requirements of an IBM-compatible PC together with typical current and power ratings. The +5 V rail provides power to all TTL applications. The +12 V line is needed to drive the motors of the disk drives and CD-ROMs. Some applications such as a serial port require bipolar (i.e. positive and negative) electrical supplies. This is provided by the −5 V and −12 V rails. All voltages are subject to a tight regulation of ±5 per cent. For the 5 V supply, this means a maximum of 5.25 V and a minimum of 4.75 V, and for the 12 V supply, a maximum of 12.6 V and a minimum of 11.4 V. When the power supply is not connected to any load, its output voltage falls to zero.

Table 3.1 Power supply requirements

Voltage (V)	Colour	Current (A)	Power (W)
+5	Red	20.0	100
−5	White	0.5	2.5
+12	Yellow	8.0	96.0
−12V	Blue	0.5	6.0

The switched mode power supply

Compared with the linear type, the switched power supply is more efficient and therefore generates less heat and requires less space. These advantages more than compensate for its complex circuitry. For this reason, switched power supplies are universally used in computers.

Low voltage processors

Some CMOS and NMOS processors require a 3.3 or 3.45 V supply. This is obtained from the +5 V rail itself using a subassembly. ATX motherboards require direct low voltage supplies, and power units supplying these motherboards have extra 3.3/3.45 V outputs.

Power rating

The power rating of a power supply is the total amount of power it can deliver in watts. It can be calculated by multiplying each of the four voltages by their individual current rating and adding up the results. Most modern PCs need power supplies with a power rating of between 220 and 280 W. More powerful computers with multiple hard disk drives or numerous optional extras require more powerful supplies to ensure that they can meet the loading requirements of the system. A fuse rating of 2 A is usually used.

Overcurrent and other protection

In addition to voltage outputs, a computer power supply has a number of protection circuits to minimise damage to the chips by permanent or intermittent faults. The first of these is overcurrent protection which is a mandatory specification. Overcurrent protection will shut the supply down if more than a safe current is drawn from it. This may be caused by a short circuit on the motherboard itself or on other devices or subsystem. On the other hand it could be a result of a low power rating of the power supply itself. The shutdown will continue until the power switch is recycled (switched off and on again). A good quality power supply should protect the computer against short duration dips in the mains voltage of, say, 50 to 100 ms. It should also incorporate an automatic restart following a short period of undervoltage from the mains, known as a brown-out. A few seconds' delay is normally included to the restart time to give any peripherals and the subsystem time to reset before the system starts up again. Power supplies should also be protected against excessive heat by a thermal cut-out which shuts the power off. A delay on restart is usually included. The power supply will also shut down if the cooling fan fails to rotate. This could be caused by a malfunctioning fan or by a failure in the 12 V line which drives the electric fan. Finally, the power supply will shut down if none of its outputs is connected to a load.

The power-good (PG) signal

The power-good (PG) signal is generated by the power supply when all its internal tests have been passed and a stabilised output is established. This normally takes between 0.1 and 0.5 seconds after power has been turned on. The PG signal is used to generate a power-up reset signal to start up the processor as shown in Fig. 3.1. When the PG signal goes HIGH, capacitor C_1 charges up through R_1. When the capacitor is fully charged, pin 11 ($\overline{\text{RES}}$) on the 82284/84A goes HIGH and the clock generator starts oscillating. Following a short period of time, pin 12 (RESET) goes HIGH taking the $\overline{\text{RES}}$ pin of the processor HIGH to start up the system. The circuit in Fig. 3.1 includes a push button for a manual reset of the processor. Alternatively, a reset may be invoked by simply taking the PG signal to ground via a 1k resistor.

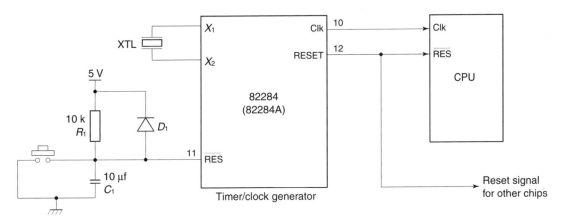

Figure 3.1 PC reset via the timer/clock generator

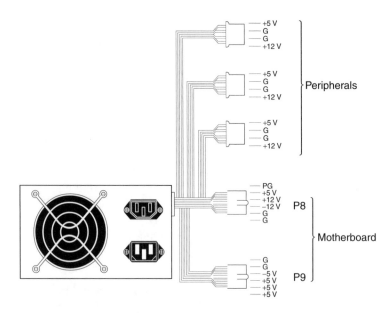

Figure 3.2 Power supply outputs

Power supply connectors All PC-compatible power supplies have two kinds of connectors coming out of the box: two 6-way connectors for the motherboard and three or four 4-way connectors as shown in Fig. 3.2.

The two motherboard power connectors (designated P8 and P9 in Fig. 3.2) are plugged into the motherboard with the black leads (GND) adjacent to each other as shown in Fig. 3.3. The function of each connector lead is listed in Table 3.2.

Power supplies serving ATX motherboards have two 10-pin connectors, a total of 20 leads, to accomodate the extra 3.3/3.4 V supplies.

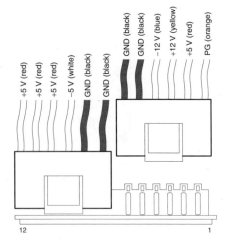

Figure 3.3 Motherboard power connectors

Table 3.2 Colour and function of motherboard power connector leads

Pin	Colour	Function
1	Orange	PG
2	Red	+5 V
3	Yellow	+12 V
4	Blue	−12 V
5	Black	GND
6	Black	GND
7	Black	GND
8	Black	GND
9	White	−5 V
10	Red	+5 V
11	Red	+5 V
12	Red	+5 V

4 Computer memory

A computer cannot work without some form of memory to store programs and routines. Computer memory is used to store the sequence of instructions and related data which form what is known as a program or routine. It is also used to store temporary or permanent data used or created by the program. In running a program, the CPU will need to access the memory store at a rate of between 10 and 50 MHz.

In theory, any type of memory store, including a disk drive, can be used provided it is large enough to store the program instructions and associated data. However, because disk drives are extremely slow compared with the speed of the CPU, using them as the main processor memory would make the whole system very slow. The processor will spend more of its time waiting to access the disk drive than carrying out program instructions. For this reason, the main memory where application and other support programs are loaded must have a speed comparable with that of the CPU itself. This means a memory store in the form of integrated circuits or chips. A small amount of memory is also provided by the processor itself.

Memory chips   Memory chips have two main properties that determine their application: storage capacity or size and access time or speed.

A memory chip contains a number of locations, each of which stores one or more bits of data known as its bit width. The storage capacity of a memory chip is the product of the number of locations and the bit width. For example, a chip with 512 locations and a 2-bit data width, has a memory size of

$$512 \times 2 = 1024 \text{ bits}$$

Since the standard unit of data is a byte (8 bits), the above storage capacity is normally given as

$$1024/8 = 128 \text{ bytes}$$

The number of locations may be obtained from the address width of the chip. For example, a chip with 10 address lines has $2^{10} = 1024$ or

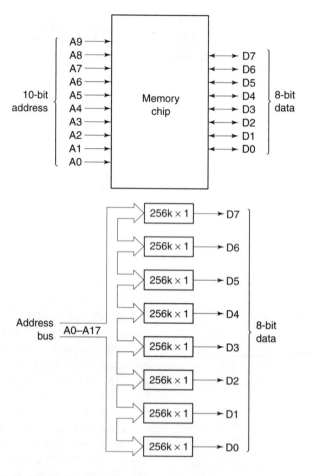

Figure 4.1 Memory chip address and data lines

Figure 4.2 Memory bank

1k locations. Given an 8-bit data width, a 10-bit address chip (Fig. 4.1) has a memory size of

$$2^{10} \times 8 = 1024 \times 8 = 1k \times 1 \text{ byte} = 1\text{kbyte or } 1\text{KB}$$

A single chip is usually insufficient to provide the memory requirements of a computer. A number of chips are therefore connected in parallel to form what is known as a memory bank. Fig. 4.2 shows a memory bank consisting of eight 1-bit chips. Each chip has 18 address lines (A0–A17). The total storage capacity of the bank may be calculated as follows:

Capacity of one chip = $2^{18} \times 1 = 256\text{k} \times 1 = 256$ kbits
Total size of the memory bank = 256 kbits $\times$ 8 = 256KB

Access time is the speed with which a location within the memory chip may be made available to the data bus. It is defined as the time interval between the instant that an address is sent to the memory chip and the instant that the data stored into the location appears on the data bus. Access time is given in nanoseconds (ns) and varies from 25 ns to the relatively slow 200 ns.

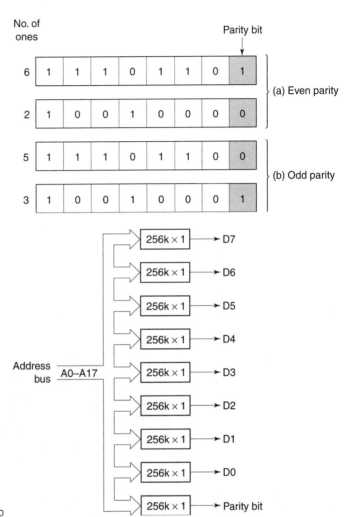

No. of
ones

Parity bit

| 6 | 1 | 1 | 1 | 0 | 1 | 1 | 0 | 1 |
| 2 | 1 | 0 | 0 | 1 | 0 | 0 | 0 | 0 |

(a) Even parity

| 5 | 1 | 1 | 1 | 0 | 1 | 1 | 0 | 0 |
| 3 | 1 | 0 | 0 | 1 | 0 | 0 | 0 | 1 |

(b) Odd parity

Figure 4.3   Even and odd parity

Address
bus   A0–A17

256k × 1 ──► D7
256k × 1 ──► D6
256k × 1 ──► D5
256k × 1 ──► D4
256k × 1 ──► D3
256k × 1 ──► D2
256k × 1 ──► D1
256k × 1 ──► D0
256k × 1 ──► Parity bit

Figure 4.4   Memory bank with parity chip

Parity checking

A memory bank may include an additional 1-bit chip for parity error checking. Parity checking involves counting the number of ones in an 8-bit data package and generating an additional ninth bit to indicate whether that count is odd or even.

There are two types of parity checking: even and odd. If, in an 8 bit word, the number of ones is odd, a parity bit at logic 1 is generated to make the number even for 'even parity' (Fig. 4.3). Conversely, a parity bit of 0 is generated to make the number of ones odd for 'odd parity'. A single parity generator/detector chip may be programmed to generate the parity or to check for correct parity. If a wrong parity is detected, the CPU is interrupted by a special non-maskable interrupt (NMI), and a special routine is then executed which displays a parity error message on the screen. Where parity is utilised, a separate parity chip is used for that purpose. Fig. 4.4 shows the same memory bank as that shown in Fig. 4.2 with a ninth chip for parity. Normally, the parity chip can be identified by its size compared with the data chips. Fig. 4.5 illustrates a memory bank consisting of four 2-bit chips and one 1-bit chip. The four 2-bit chips provide 1 byte of data and the 1-bit chip provides the associated 1 bit for parity. The capacity of the bank is given by the four 2-bit chips:

$$\text{Capacity} = 512k \times 2 \text{ bits} \times 4 = 512k \times 8 = 512KB$$

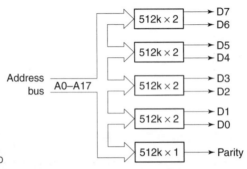

Figure 4.5   Memory bank with parity chip

Chip markings   The marking on a memory chip denotes both its size and speed. A typical arrangement is shown in Fig. 4.6. The speed in ns is indicated by a number following a dash (-). For instance, - 60 means a speed of 60. Sometimes the last digit is missing, e.g. -10. This indicates a speed of 100 ns since the fastest possible access time is 20 ns. Neglecting the speed, the last two or three numbers from the right record the number of locations in k. This number has to be of a standard size, i.e. 64k, 128k, 256k and 512k; 1M is usually indicated by 1000, 1024, 100 or 10 and 4M by 4000 or 400. The number to the left of the size is the data width in bits. Hence, TMS841128 - 7 indicates a 128k × 1 bit chip with an access time of 70 ns. Further examples of chip markings are given in Appendix 4.

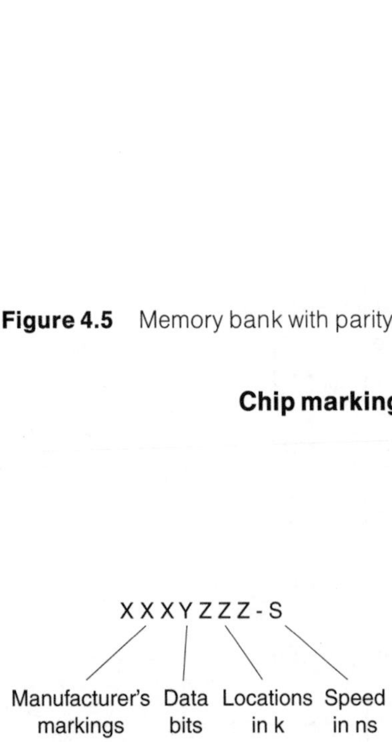

X X X Y Z Z Z - S

Manufacturer's   Data   Locations   Speed
markings   bits   in k   in ns

Figure 4.6   Memory chip markings

Types of memory chips   **Random access memory**

Random access memory (RAM) is a volatile memory chip which the user may read from or write to, and hence it is also known as read/write memory. Locations may be accessed at random by placing the address of the selected location onto the address lines. The pin-out requirements of a RAM chip are shown in Fig. 4.7. Apart from the address lines and the data bits, there are three control lines all of which are active low: write enable (WE) which goes LOW when the CPU wishes to write new data into the selected location; output enable (OE) which goes LOW when the processor wishes to read the contents of the location; and chip select (CS) which is driven LOW when the selected location falls within the address range assigned for the chip.

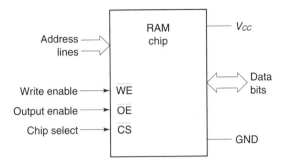

Figure 4.7 Memory chip pin allocation

There are two major categories of RAMs: Dynamic RAM (DRAM) and Static RAM (SRAM). DRAMs store information in the form of a charge on a capacitor. However, owing to leakage, the charge is lost and has to be restored at frequent intervals of between 2 and 4 ms, a process which is known as 'refreshing' the cell. DRAMs have the advantage of higher density and very low power consumption. SRAM devices employ flip-flops (electronic switching devices) as the basic cell and hence require no refreshing. They will hold data as long as d.c. power continues to be applied to the device. SRAMs are very fast with an access time of 20 ns or less compared with 60 ns for DRAMs. However, they are more expensive than the dynamic type, which inhibits their use as the main memory store of a computer system.

Multiplexing

Because of their low cost and high density, DRAM devices are used to provide the bulk of computer memory of a few megabytes. The number of address pins required to accommodate this size of memory becomes physically inhibitive for manufacturing purposes. To overcome this problem, address multiplexing is employed as shown in Fig. 4.8. The multiplexer receives the full 20-bit address from the address bus which is then fed to the memory chip in two stages. First, A0–A9 are fed to the address pins on the IC followed by A10–A19 which are fed to the same IC pins. Two special control signals, $\overline{CAS}$, the column address strobe, and $\overline{RAS}$, the row address strobe, are provided to route the two halves to two internal latches. The full address is then held within the IC long enough to access the data in the selected location.

Non-volatile RAM (NV-RAM)

One method of preserving the stored data in a normal RAM is to employ back-up batteries to maintain the d.c. supply voltage to the chip when the mains supply is removed. To avoid the use of back-up batteries, non-volatile RAM (NV-RAM) may be used in which each

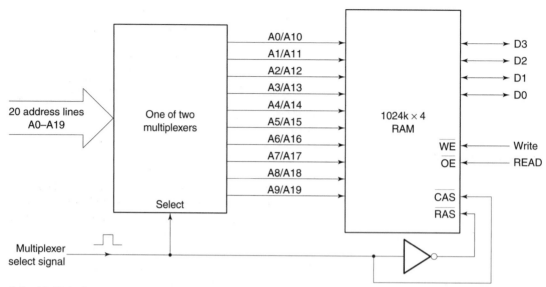

Figure 4.8   Multiplexing

cell has a shadow non-volatile storage transistor. The data is entered into the cells as normal but it can be transferred to the non-volatile storage cells when an enable signal is used. The main disadvantage of this type of device is its low component density requiring about five times the chip area of a normal RAM for the same storage capacity. Another disadvantage of NV-RAMs is their relatively long access time.

Read only memories (ROMs)

Although computer memory is mainly RAM, ROM devices are also necessary to store the start-up program, configuration details, input/output routines and conversion tables. Compared with RAM, ROM devices are slow with a typical access time in excess of 200 ns. This makes them unsuitable for applications that require fast memory access, such as video graphics. There are several types of ROM devices, some of which are described below.

Mask ROM is a non-volatile memory used for storing data permanently. The data stored can only be read by the user and no new data can be written into the device. ROM devices are programmed by the manufacturer in accordance with predetermined specifications. Once entered the data cannot be altered subsequently. PROM (Programmable Read Only Memory) devices fulfil the same basic function as ROM devices except that they may be programmed by the user, a process known as 'blowing' the chip. Once programmed, PROMs cannot be altered.

EPROM (Erasable Programmable Read Only Memory) devices overcome this by allowing the user to delete or erase the stored data and thus change the program. The stored program in an EPROM may be erased by exposing the memory cells to ultraviolet light through a 'window' on the IC package. This process takes 20 to 30 minutes at the end of which the IC is in a 'blank state' ready to be reprogrammed.

EEPROM (Electrically Erasable Programable Read Only Memory) devices can be programmed and erased while still connected to the circuit by the application of suitable electrical signals. Furthermore, individual locations may be erased and programmed without interfering with the rest of the data pattern. As a result of overwriting locations, EEPROM has a comparatively short life span.

Flash RAM

An advance to the EEPROM is the flash RAM. Once again all locations may be erased and reprogrammed except this time using normal voltages that are available in the PC. However, flash RAM continues to suffer from a short life span and a long access time of between 60 and 150 ns.

Comparison table   The following table shows a comparison of the various devices:

	DRAM	SRAM	ROM	EPROM	EEPROM	Flash
Capacity	Mbytes	kbytes	kbytes	kbytes	kbytes	kbytes
Speed (ns)	60–120	25–40	200	400	400	100
Life span	Long	Long	Long	Short	Short	Short

Real and protected mode

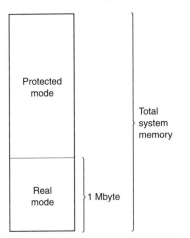

Figure 4.9 Real and protected mode

The original XT computer used the Intel 8086 microprocessor with a total memory of 1MB of RAM space. DOS was therefore designed to work within a 1 MB boundary. When the AT computers were introduced with Intel's 80286 microprocessor, 16MB of memory was made available for the processor to address. However, to ensure backward compatibility, i.e. to ensure that adaptors and application programs designed to work with the original XT could continue to be used with the AT system, the 1MB limit was retained. A computer operating within the 1MB limit was then said to be operating in the real mode (Fig. 4.9). In order to address memory locations above the 1MB boundary a special device driver (or program) was required and the computer was then said to operate in the protected mode. The commercial needs for backward compatibility perceived by MS-DOS designers have perpetuated this unhelpful dual mode of operation. Other operating systems like OS/2 are designed without the artificial 1MB boundary limit and Windows incorporates a memory manager to cope with protected mode operation.

Computer software requirement

A computer performs its operations by the execution of software programs. The main software program is the application program such as a word processor, database or game. To launch an application program, DOS is instructed to load a file with an .EXE or a .COM extension from a disk drive, a CD-ROM or any other mass storage device, into the system's RAM. Other program data files may also be loaded into RAM for the program to be executed, and as long as the application package is running, these files must continue to reside in RAM.

Apart from the application program itself, a PC requires a number of other programs in order to perform a number of different tasks such as generating a video display, controlling a mouse and executing DOS commands. These programs are known as memory resident software and are loaded into system memory (RAM) at the boot-up stage.

There are two types of memory resident software: transient and utility. Transient programs include:

- the internal commands (resident) part of DOS;
- system configuration and basic input/output routines;
- device drivers such as programs to operate a mouse or a network or memory management programs, e.g. HIMEM.SYS;
- terminate and stay resident (TSR) routines which remain in memory until activated, usually by a keystroke combination.

Utility programs include such routines as system BIOS, video/graphic display programs, and other programs which control optional devices such as a mouse, a CD-ROM drive or a sound card.

Where these programs are provided on ROM or PROM packages, they still occupy and must be allocated a space within the total memory of the system.

Memory map

When DOS was designed with the introduction of the XT computer, it accommodated both application and memory resident programs within the 1MB boundary. Furthermore, DOS software dictates that application programs must occupy contiguous memory locations, i.e. a memory space with no gaps in the entire range from the beginning to the end.

The original 1MB of real mode memory was divided into two parts: a lower 640KB, known as conventional or base memory for loading the application program as well as the transient programs, and an upper 384KB known as the upper memory area (UMA) for utility programs (Fig. 4.10). Backward compatibility made it necessary for this division to continue and until the advent of modern memory management techniques, DOS applications were limited in size to fit within the 640KB of contiguous base memory. Memory space above 1MB is known as extended (protected mode)

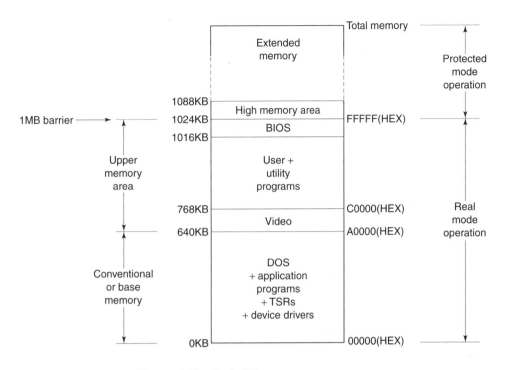

Figure 4.10   Basic PC memory map

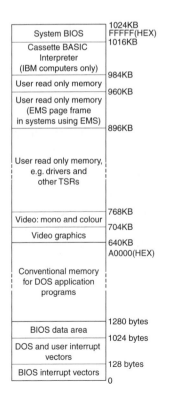

Figure 4.11   1 MB memory map

memory. The table showing the allocation of memory addresses and the locations of various programs is known as the memory map of the computer (Fig. 4.11).

Although in theory, 640KB are available for software applications, in practice a large chunk of conventional memory may be occupied by memory resident programs such as device drivers and TSRs. One way of maximising the memory available for DOS application programs is by loading these programs into unused upper memory spaces thus freeing precious base memory.

The high memory area

The internal architecture of Intel processors does not permit the use of full linear addressing of memory location. In its place a segment:offset technique is employed. A spin-off of this technique makes it possible to address the first 64KB of extended memory, known as the high memory area (HMA), in the real mode (Fig. 4.10). Provided an appropriate memory management program is used, such as HIMEM.SYS, the 64KB HMA may be treated in exactly the same way as the upper memory area. DOS versions 5.0 onwards provide for DOS-resident programs to be loaded into the HMA thus freeing some 45KB or more of conventional memory.

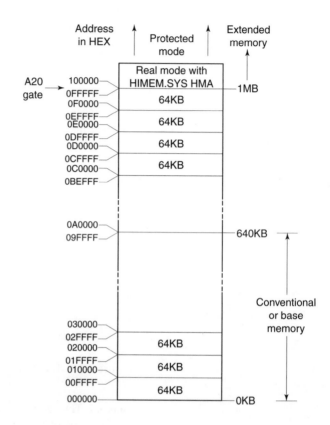

Figure 4.12 Memory segments

Memory addressing and the A20 gate

Real mode memory addresses in Intel processors are established by an overlapping segment address and an offset address. Both the segment and the offset are 16-bit numbers. For simplicity, hexadecimal digits are used, e.g. 0000:0200 (segment = 0000, offset = 0200) or A000:1000 (segment = A000, offset = 1000).

The segment address defines the beginning of the 64KB memory segment. For instance, segment 3000 has a starting address of 30000 and segment D000 has a starting address of D0000. Thus, the XT 1MB memory is divided into 16 × 64KB segments as shown in Fig. 4.12. The offset address, on the other hand, selects a location within that segment.

The segment:offset method of addressing allows programs to be relocated in system memory by simply changing the segment address within the processor. Application programs can then be loaded into any compatible PC regardless of the size and structure of its memory.

The full linear address is obtained by shifting the segment four binary places (or one hexadecimal digit) to the left and adding it to the offset. For example, address 0000:0200 gives rise to the following linear address:

```
segment          0000
offset      +    0200  (shifted one place to the right)
linear address   00200
```

and address A000:1000 gives rise to

```
segment          A000
offset      +    1000
linear address   A1000
```

The highest address that may be set by this method is FFFF:FFFF which yields a linear address of

```
segment          FFFF
offset      +    FFFF
linear address   10FFEF
```

Linear address 10FFEF falls within the HMA. Such a location had no significance for 8088/86 systems which had only 20 address lines. However, with the 286 and higher processors, such a location may be addressed by the processor provided the 21st address line known as the A20 gate is enabled, in which case all but 16 bytes of the 64KB HMA can be addressed in the real mode.

Extended memory system (XMS)

As mentioned previously, the memory of a system based on the 286 or higher processors can extend beyond the 1MB boundary that exists when the processor is operating in real mode. On the 286, the memory limit is 16MB and on the 386-, 486- and Pentium-based systems, the limit is 4GB (4096MB).

To access extended memory locations, the segment:offset addressing scheme must be changed. Whilst the offset continues to be used to locate an address within the segment, the segment itself is replaced by a descriptor which, among other things, relocates the segment into extended memory. As far as DOS is concerned, the segment plus offset still defines the memory location and real mode operations can take place.

Such a system allows programs the freedom to use any part of extended memory, which may result in the same memory space being used by different programs. In order to prevent this from taking place, an extended memory system (XMS) specification was developed by Microsoft, Intel, AST Corporation and Lotus Development. XMS is introduced to the system by loading an extended memory manager driver such as HIMEM.SYS or QEMM into system RAM. As mentioned earlier, such memory management techniques are irrelevant to a system such as OS/2 because it is a protected mode operating system designed to use extended memory.

Expanded memory system (EMS)

Unlike extended memory, expanded memory is not addressable by the processor. Instead, it is accessed through a small 64KB window

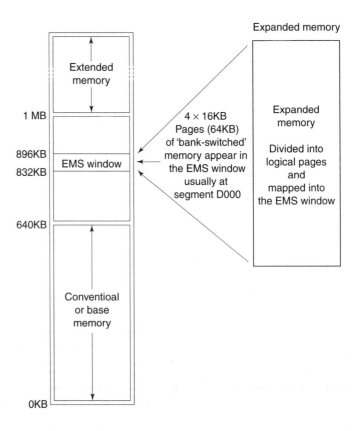

Figure 4.13 Expanded memory technique

created in the upper memory area by a process known as bank switching (Fig. 4.13). The process is regulated by a memory manager in accordance with agreed expanded memory system (EMS) specifications.

The EMS specification involves dividing expanded memory into 16KB segments called pages. Each page contains program-coded instructions or data. The contents of these pages may then be copied (or mapped) into a page window or frame inside the reserved area of the UMA as and when required by the processor. In this way, the processor can address the contents of the page frame in real mode. The page frames are continuously updated by the processor.

Compared with extended memory, EMS techniques are very slow. For this reason, expanded memory is not normally used. Where it has to be used, for programs which employ EMS, an expanded memory driver program, EMM386. EXE, is utilised which allows extended memory to simulate expanded memory.

Logical and physical memory

As far as a computer program is concerned, memory is organised into byte size locations known as the logical memory map. Fig. 4.14 illustrates the logical memory map for Intel processors. For the 8086/88, logical memory consists of 1MB starting at 00000 (HEX)

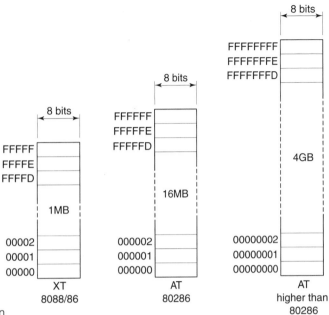

Figure 4.14 Logical memory organisation

and finishing at FFFFF (HEX). The 286 processor provides a total of 16MB starting at 000000 and finishing at FFFFFF and so on.

Processors may address 8-bit data (1 byte) or 16-bit data (2 bytes), known as a word, or 32-bit data (4 bytes) known as a double word. Addressing a 16-bit word, the processor has to access 2 bytes stored in two consecutive locations. For example, word F1F2H (H indicates a HEX number) at location 00A23H is actually stored in the following two locations:

00A23H for the least significant byte (low byte), F0
00A24H for the most significant byte (high byte), F1

If a 32-bit double word is to be accessed, four consecutive locations have to be addressed. For example, double word F1F0E1E0 at location 00A23 will be stored in the following locations:

00A23H	E0 (low byte)
00A24H	E1
00A25H	F0
00A26H	F1 (high byte)

Except for the 8088, a computer must therefore be able to access two or more locations simultaneously. This is made possible by the organisation of memory devices into 16- and 32-bit memory banks as shown in Fig. 4.15. A bank may consist of one, two or four 8-bit memory blocks or slots to provide access to 8-bit, 16-bit or 32-bit data respectively.

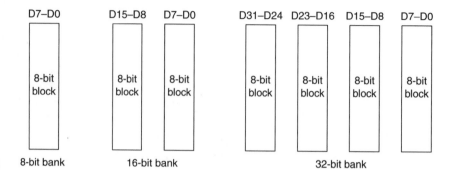

Figure 4.15 Physical memory organisation

Memory physical organisation Earlier computer systems employed discrete memory chips. A bank thus consisted of eight 1-bit memory chips (nine if parity is included), or four 2-bit memory chips (plus one 1-bit chip for parity), or two 4-bit memory chips (plus one 1-bit chip for parity) as shown in Fig. 4.16. A typical 286 memory store consisting of two 16-bit banks is shown in the figure. Each bank contains two 8-bit blocks with each block consisting of eight (+ 1) 256k 1-bit chips slotted into individual sockets. The total capacity may be calculated as follows:

Chip capacity = 265 × 1 bits = 256 bits
Block capacity = 256 × 8 = 256KB
Bank capacity = 256 × 2 = 512KB
Total capacity = 512 × 2 = 1024KB = 1 MB

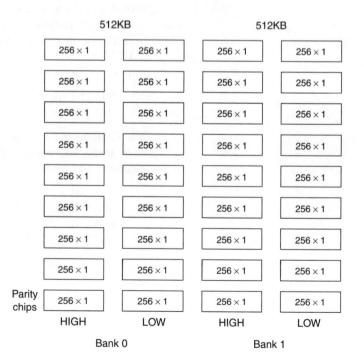

Figure 4.16 1MB memory 16-bit memory banks

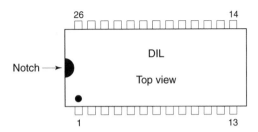

Figure 4.17   The dual-in-line package

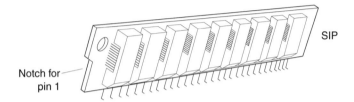

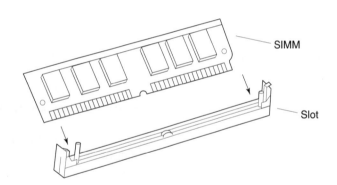

Figure 4.18   The single-in-line pin (SIP) and the single-in-line memory module (SIMM)

Memory packaging

The basic package of a memory device is the dual-in-line (DIL) shown in Fig. 4.17. An alternative to the individual memory chip is the memory module. Individual chips are mounted onto printed circuit boards in 8-bit, 16-bit or 32-bit format. Access to the chips is provided by protruding pins (single-in-line pin, SIP) or edge contacts (single-in-line memory module, SIMM) as shown in Fig. 4.18. SIMMs are universally used in modern computers because of their large capacity, small size and the ease with which they can be replaced (there are no pins to bend). SIMMs are provided in two formats:

30-pin: 9-bit (8 + 1 for parity) module, Fig. 4.19a.
72-pin: 36-bit (32 + 4 for parity) module, Fig. 4.19b.

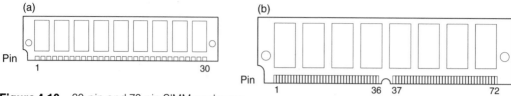

Figure 4.19   30-pin and 72-pin SIMM packages

SIMMs are available both with and without parity and until recently all compatible PCs were designed with parity checking.

DIMM

Memory packages are also provided in a 168-pin dual-in-line memory module (DIMM) (Fig. 4.20). DIMMs are available in 64-bit packages with large storage capacities.

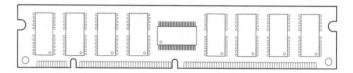

Figure 4.20   DIMM banks

Typical memory organisation using SIMMs

The number of SIMMs in a memory bank is determined by the data width of the system and the type of SIMM used. For instance, a 16-bit 386 motherboard requires two 30-pin SIMMs per bank (Fig. 4.21a) while a 32-bit 486 motherboard requires four 30-pin SIMM

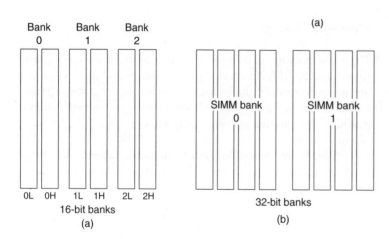

Figure 4.21   The SIMM (DRAM) package

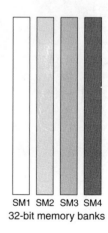

Figure 4.22   The SIMM (DRAM) package

per bank (Fig. 4.21b). Where 72-pin SIMM slots are provided, only one SIMM slot per bank is necessary for a 32-bit 386, 486 or Pentium (Fig. 4.22).

Rules for filling bank slots

1. All slots in a bank must be filled. Banks cannot be left partly empty.
2. All memory modules in a given bank must have the same memory capacity.
3. All modules should have the same speed otherwise the module with the slowest speed will dominate.
4. Bank 0 must have the lowest capacity, followed by bank 1 and so on.
5. Bank 0 must be filled before bank 1 and so on.

In some computer systems, banks are interchangeable. In this case, rules 3 and 4 above need not apply.

Wait states

In cases where the speed of the processor is faster than the access time of the memory devices, one or more wait states have to be introduced to slow the CPU down. A wait state causes the processor to suspend its activities for one or more clock cycles to allow slower memory to catch up. The number of wait states that are required depends on the speed of memory and the type of CPU used. Some computer systems provide automatic wait state detection and settings. Wait states curtail computer performance drastically. With one wait state, a PC operates at two-thirds of its potential speed; two wait states cut the performance by half.

Cache memory

The only way to avoid wait states as processor speed improves is to use faster memory devices. The most straightforward way of increasing the speed of computer memory is to use fast SRAM chips. The cost of SRAM chips coupled with their low packing density make their extensive use inhibitive. The use of SRAM devices has to be more targeted and specific to make economic sense. To this end, the cache memory technique was introduced. Motherboards which support cache memory have a set of IC socket holders or a SRAM 160-pin DIMM slot available, into which SRAM chips or SRAM modules (Fig. 4.23) may be inserted as outlined by the manufacturer's handbook. Where a SRAM DIMM is used, a single package may be used to provide 256KB or 512KB cache memory.

The cache memory technique involves the use of a block of few kilobytes (8–512KB) of fast SRAM to store the contents of the most frequently accessed RAM locations and the part of the program that

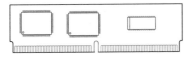

Figure 4.23

the processor is most likely to call for. The identification of these instructions and data and loading them into the cache memory block is carried out by a cache controller which continuously updates the contents of cache memory as necessary. The processor will first attempt to fetch instructions or data from the fast cache memory. If they are not available, wait states will be introduced and the processor will access the slow DRAM locations to fetch the desired information. With a hit rate (i.e. the likelihood of the processor finding what it wants in cache) as high as 95 per cent, the net effect is that the system acts as though nearly all its memory is made up of very fast SRAM.

The cache controller has to keep a record of the information copied into cache, and where it is stored. A small memory known as tag memory is used for this purpose.

A faster and a more effective cache memory was introduced with fourth-generation processors (486 upwards). These processors are built with on-chip internal cache memory known as level 1 (L1) cache of between 8 and 16KB with a very fast access time of between 5 and 10 ns.

Burst mode

The speed of reading cache memory location may be increased by the burst mode technique introduced with the 486 processor. This technique uses the fact that programs usually access locations in sequence, allowing the processor to carry out four sequential data transfers without an intervening address cycle.

Write-back cache

The cache technique described above speeds up the process of reading memory locations by accessing a cache location instead of a main memory location. Writing into memory, on the other hand, continues to take place at the slower speed determined by the DRAM chips of the main memory. This is because of the necessary synchronous operation of cache memory which ensures that cache memory locations have the same contents as the corresponding locations they mirror in main memory. Cache and main memory locations must therefore be updated, i.e. written into simultaneously with all the wasteful wait states. This process is known as write-through.

A new technique known as write-back allows the processor to write changes to cache memory, which speeds up the process. The changes made to the cache are subsequently transferred to the corresponding main memory locations by the cache controller when some spare time becomes available.

Other fast memory techniques There are several other methods to improve memory speeds and thus avoid wait states. One such method is the use of special RAM chips that combine the features of both dynamic and static RAM devices, such as page mode RAM and static column RAM. Another technique is memory interleaving or memory banking, which may improve performance by as much as 75 per cent. This technique involves dividing system memory into two or four interleaved banks. Sequential bytes are held on alternate banks so the processor will step from one bank to the other as it carries out its tasks. The CPU, having read one bank and while it is waiting for its request to be met, can read the other bank without the need for a wait state. The advantage of this technique (used extensively in 286-based systems) is that it does not require special memory chips. However, it only works while reading logically sequential bytes.

Extended data out (EDO)

Modern computers use special DRAM devices known as extended data out (EDO) to improve the system memory speed. This is carried out by keeping the output signal from the EDO chip valid for a longer period of time. The use of EDO can save one wait state compared with the page mode technique at no extra cost.

Video RAM (VRAM)

Another special DRAM chip which provides fast access time is the video RAM (VRAM). Two independent data paths are provided by VRAM chips: one input path and one output path. Memory locations can thus be read and written at the same time, an essential feature for fast video/graphic displays.

Rambus DRAM (RDRAM)

RDRAM is a very fast, high density memory chip which employs a dedicated bus known as Rambus. Capacities of up to 64 megabits per chip are available which can operate at 100 MHz or over with a data transfer rate of 500 megabits per second.

DEBUG

DEBUG is a DOS routine designed to help find errors in programs – hence the name. It allows the user to look into the contents of memory locations and registers. It may also be used to investigate

```
-DFFFF:0000
FFFF:0000  EA D4 04 99 02 30 37 2F-32 35 2F 39 34 00 FC 00   .....07/25/94...
FFFF:0010  00 00 00 56 44 49 53 4B-33 2E 33 80 00 01 01 00   ...VDISK3.3.....
FFFF:0020  01 40 00 00 02 FE 06 00-80 00 01 00 00 00 40 04   .@............@.
FFFF:0030  70 00 2E 8E 06 30 00 BF-E0 06 B9 04 00 AB 47 47   p....0........GG
FFFF:0040  E2 FB CB 56 50 51 52 57-55 1E 06 53 8B EC 8B 76   ...VPQRWU..S...v
FFFF:0050  12 2E 8E 1E 30 00 8B 44-02 A2 21 00 88 26 E7 04   ....0..D..!..&..
FFFF:0060  8B 34 C4 1E 12 00 26 8A-47 01 26 8A 67 0D 26 8B   .4....&.G.&.g.&.
FFFF:0070  4F 12 26 8B 57 14 81 FE-A2 04 75 17 C7 06 2B 05   O.&.W.....u...+.
```

Figure 4.24

the configuration of a computer system by displaying the appropriate set of memory locations.

The DEBUG routine is called by typing DEBUG at the C: prompt. The computer will respond by displaying the DEBUG prompt which is usually a dash (-). Commands such as -D for dump and -E for edit may then be entered.

The dump, -D, command allows the user to display 128 bytes of memory starting at the address specified by the command. The address must be specified in the segment:offset format. For instance, to display 128 bytes of memory starting at address FFFF:0000, the command to be entered is

-DFFFF:0000

The computer will respond with the display shown in Fig. 4.24. The middle part of the display lists the contents of memory locations, byte by byte. Each line lists 16 bytes stored in 16 locations starting at the address specified in the left hand section of the display. Eight lines are shown, which adds up to $8 \times 16 = 128$ bytes. For instance, starting at the first line, location FFFF:0000 contains EA, location FFFF:0001 contains D4 and so on to location FFFF:000F which contains 00. The next location starts at the second line with FFFF:0010 containing 00 and so on. The right hand section of the display lists the ASCII character that corresponds to the byte listed. Where the byte does not correspond to an ASCII character, a dot (.) is displayed. In Fig. 4.24, the BIOS date is displayed in the ASCII section for the display. This is because the memory locations FFFF:0006 to FFFF:000D contain that information. Other information may also be listed, such as the DOS version which is contained within IO.SYS. The contents of IO.SYS may be displayed by the following command from the DOS prompt:

C:\>DEBUG IO.SYS

The first 128 bytes of IO.SYS will be displayed. By simply entering D at the debug command, the next 128 bytes of IO.SYS will be

```
FFFF:1C70   44 4F 53 20 56 65 72 73-69 6F 6E 20 36 20 28 43   DOS Version 6 (C
FFFF:1C80   29 43 6F 70 79 72 69 67-68 74 20 31 39 38 31 2D   )Copyright 1981-
FFFF:1C90   31 39 39 33 20 4D 69 63-72 6F 73 6F 66 74 20 43   1993 Microsoft C
FFFF:1CA0   6F 72 70 20 4C 69 63 65-6E 73 65 64 20 4D 61 74   orp Licensed Mat
FFFF:1CB0   65 72 69 61 6C 20 2D 20-50 72 6F 70 65 72 74 79   erial - Property
FFFF:1CC0   20 6F 66 20 4D 69 63 72-6F 73 6F 66 74 20 41 6C    of Microsoft Al
FFFF:1CD0   6C 20 72 69 67 68 74 73-20 72 65 73 65 72 76 65   l rights reserve
FFFF:1CE0   64 20 3C 06 73 03 B0 FF-CF 1E 2E 8E 1E E7 3D 50   d <.v.........=P
```
—

Figure 4.25

displayed and so on. A display similar to that shown in Fig. 4.25 may thus be produced. A similar procedure may be followed with MSDOS.SYS.

5 The motherboard

The motherboard, or system board, is the heart of any computer system. It contains all the main circuitry of the computer as well as the main components such as the processor, support chips, BIOS ROM and memory devices. The motherboard may also provide on-board disk and video controllers, I/O adaptor chips and other peripheral functions such as a CD-ROM controller. However, these functions could be provided by the use of expansion cards which are plugged into expansion slots provided on the motherboard.

For a long time, the design and layout of motherboards of compatible PCs followed that of the IBM format. However, the development of VLSI ASICs (Application Specific Integrated Circuits) has resulted in fewer and fewer chips being required to carry out the functions of the motherboard and consequently different layouts. Fig. 5.1 illustrates a generalised layout of a motherboard. Apart from general purpose logic devices such as gates, multiplexers and decoders, the motherboard has a central core of functions that are carried out by VLSI devices including the CPU. The processor communicates with all other devices via a bus structure.

Motherboard components   The following are the component parts of a motherboard:

The processor. The central processing unit or microprocessor determines the processing power of the motherboard as well as the type of software that may be used.

The coprocessor. Also known as the maths or numeric processor unit (NPU), a coprocessor is a programmable logic device designed to handle what is known as floating-point mathematical operations. A coprocessor may be provided as a separate chip (e.g. the 80287 and the 80387) on the motherboard or incorporated on board the processor itself as is the case with the 80486 and the Pentium. Software that takes advantage of the coprocessor can realise substantial improvements to the system's performance.

Support chips. The operation of a computer involves a number of activities taking place under the control of the CPU. These activities are carried out by dedicated VLSI chips known as support chips, such as a clock generator and interrupt and DMA controllers.

Main system memory. The motherboard incorporates the system's memory banks. Modern computers employ SIMM (Single In-line Memory Module) slots for this purpose. Fig. 5.1 shows four 72-pin memory banks.

Cache memory. Modern motherboards provide IC sockets or module slots for fast cache memory chips. The size of the cache is determined by the type of motherboard used.

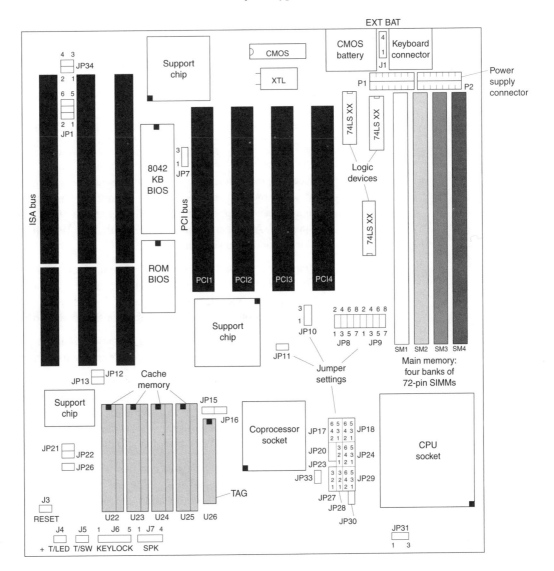

Figure 5.1   Typical motherboard layout

ROM BIOS. The BIOS routines are stored in a ROM or EPROM DIL package such as the 27PC512-15. Flash BIOS may also be used. The BIOS chip usually has a paper sticker stating the name of the manufacturer, date and version.

Keyboard controller (KBC). Also known as keyboard BIOS, this converts serial codes from the keyboard into ASCII codes that can be understood by the computer system.

CMOS chip and battery. The CMOS chip is a small battery-backed RAM device which is used to store the system's set-up information and configuration that are required by the BIOS routine when the system is initialised following a power-up or a reset. It also contains information about current time and date. The battery, which is usually soldered to the motherboard, ensures that the CMOS chip retains its data even when the system is switched off. If the battery has to be replaced, the data stored in CMOS will be lost and the system's CMOS set-up must be re-entered. The contents of CMOS may be deleted without disconnecting the battery using jumper connections. This may be necessary, for instance, in such cases when a secret password which is stored in CMOS has been mislaid.

Expansion slots. Also known as expansion buses, these provide access to the motherboard via a double-sided edge connector. There may be more than one type of expansion bus available on the motherboard. Fig. 5.1 shows two types: three 16-bit ISA (Industry Standard Architecture) and four 32-bit PCI (Peripheral Interface Connector) expansion slots.

Timing chips and crystals. The system clock is derived from a crystal-controlled oscillator to ensure accuracy and stability. A second clock signal, using a separate 14.318 MHz crystal for the ISA expansion bus, is also available on the motherboard.

Keyboard connector. A standard AT-style 5-pin (6-pin for IBM) connector to plug in the keyboard cable is provided, normally at the rear of the board.

Power supply connector. The majority of motherboards have a standard 12-pin connector to provide d.c. power to the motherboard. The ATX motherboard features a 20-pin connector which provides extra low voltage (3.3/3.45 volts) supplies.

Jumpers and DIP switches. A number of jumpers and DIP (Dual-In-line Package) switches (Fig. 5.2) are provided to configure the motherboard to the specific arrangements and requirements of the system. When upgrading or changing a motherboard, configuration jumpers and DIP switches must be set in accordance with the manufacturer's handbook. Such configuration jumper/DIP switches may include mono/colour, CPU power requirements and speed and cache memory size.

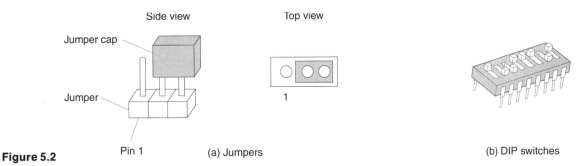

Figure 5.2 Pin 1   (a) Jumpers   (b) DIP switches

Support chips A motherboard is built around a processor and a number of support chips which provide the logic core of the system. A basic set of support chips for a PC include:

> A clock generator (82284)
> A programmable interval timer (PIT) (8254)
> A programmable interrupt controller (PIC) (8259)
> A bus controller (82288)
> A direct memory access controller (DMAC) (8237)

The system requires a number of software routines and configuration information which are stored in ROM or RAM chip devices. These are:

> A keyboard controller (KBC) (8042, 8742)
> ROM BIOS
> A CMOS set-up chip (MC146818, Dallas 1287, Dallas 1387)

Programmable devices Devices may be divided into two categories: dedicated and programmable. Dedicated devices are fabricated to carry out a particular task in a specified way, e.g. a 10 MHz clock generator. Programmable devices on the other hand are designed to carry out a particular task in several different ways, e.g. a programmable timer or counter which may be programmed to produce a number of timing signals at different frequencies or intervals. These devices contain a number of internal registers which determine their specific mode of operation. Programming such devices involves entering coded data into their registers. This is usually carried out by the processor as part of the system initialisation routine. In this way, a standard programmable chip such as PIC or PIT may be used regardless of the specific requirements of the computer in terms of configuration and peripherals. The CPU may reprogram a programmable chip at any time as necessary during the system operation simply by entering new coded data into its registers.

Motherboard architecture Fig. 5.3 illustrates the architecture for an 80286 AT motherboard. The motherboard has two bus structures: a fast CPU bus, also known as a local bus, and the slower system bus. The CPU bus operates at

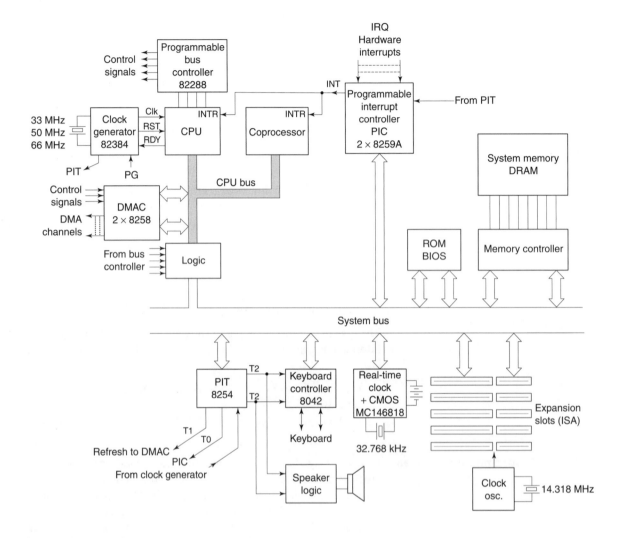

Figure 5.3 The AT motherboard architecture

the speed of the processor itself and serves the coprocessor and system memory, DRAM. The system bus invariably operates at a slower speed; hence the need for a logic circuit acting as an interface between the two bus structures. The number of bits used in each bus is determined by the CPU, e.g. 24 address and 16 data bits for a 386SX, and 32 address and 32 data bits for a 486DX. Access to the bus is provided by a programmable bus controller (82288).

There are typically two timer ICs: one at 14.318 MHz for the most commonly used ISA expansion bus, and the clock generator (82384) which among other things provides clock pulses for the processor. Both oscillators are crystal controlled for accuracy and stability; the oscillating frequency is stamped on the crystal. The clock generator also provides the reset signal for the CPU and a 1.19 MHz clock to the programmable interval timer (PIT) (8254). The PIT produces three timing channels: T0, T1 and T2. Channel T0 is an 18.2 Hz pulse which drives the real-time clock and provides an interrupt to initiate the programmable interrupt controller (PIC). The second timing channel, T1, provides a trigger pulse every 15 ms to start a DRAM refresh cycle. The third timing channel, T2, provides the interrupt signal to the keyboard controller (KBC) and the input to the speaker logic circuit. The loudspeaker logic circuit produces audible coded beeps for general information and fault indication.

A real-time clock is incorporated within the CMOS set-up chip. Time pulses generated by a crystal oscillator operating at 32.768 kHz are fed into the battery-backed chip to keep accurate time and date.

The PIC (dual 8259A chips) monitors and prioritises 15 different hardware interrupts and processes them into a single IRQ signal to the CPU. The direct memory access controller (DMAC) (dual 8258 chips) monitors and processes eight different MDA channels for fast direct memory access without the intervention of the CPU.

The KBC (8042) is a special purpose chip which monitors the keyboard and decodes keystroke signals into 8-bit ASCII codes. The BIOS chip is a mask ROM, PROM or EPROM device in which the PC start-up program is stored. A memory controller is used to carry out the frequent refresh cycles with minimum involvement of the CPU.

Chipset

XT and early AT computers used individual integrated circuits for the various functions performed by the motherboard. However, in the drive to make motherboards smaller and less expensive, many individual ICs have been combined into a set of related ASICs known as chipsets to perform these same functions. For instance the interrupt and DMA controllers are brought together into a single chip, the 82C206 integrated peripheral controller or programmable peripheral controller. Similarly, system controller chips such as the 82C235, supporting an 80386SX processor, combine the functions of a dual 8237 DMA, a dual 8259A interrupt controller, an 8254 programmable timer, a 74621 memory mapper, an 82288 bus controller and an 82284 clock generator.

Power management – the green motherboard

The need to conserve power and reduce heat emission and pollution into the atmosphere has compelled manufacturers to introduce power-saving techniques. A programmable power management chip was developed to track the use of high demand units such as video display units and hard disks. When these units are idle for a predetermined period of time, they are turned off by the IC. Power management has been improved with the incorporation of the system management mode (SMM) into the 80486 and Pentium processors.

6 The Intel processor

In IBM computers and all compatibles, the processor chip belongs to the Intel 80 x 86 family, such as the 80286, 80386, 80486 and the recent Pentium (80586). Although the original design of these processors was carried out by the US chip manufacturer Intel, processors in many compatible PCs are manufactured by one of a number of firms such as AMD (Advance Micro Devices), KTD, Cyrix, NEC and IBM. Such processors are Intel compatible and therefore able to handle the same software as the Intel chips and essentially meet the same specifications.

Processor architecture   A basic architecture of a microprocessor is shown in Fig. 6.1. It comprises the following components:

The arithmetic and logic unit (ALU). The ALU carries out all mathematical and logic operations. It is recognisable by

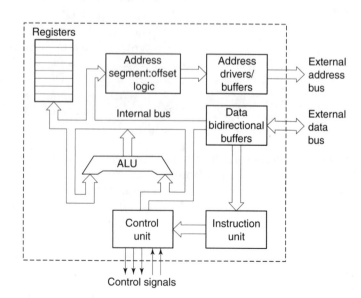

Figure 6.1   Basic microprocessor architecture

its two inputs, one for each part of the mathematical or logic operation.

Internal bus structure. This allows the various parts to communicate with each other. Communication between the internal bus and the external world is accomplished by driver/buffer interface circuits, one for the address lines and another for the data bits.

A number of registers. The processor provides a number of registers to be used as temporary stores of digital information.

Instruction unit. The instruction unit receives and stores each instruction, decodes it and informs the control unit of all the necessary steps to execute the instruction.

Address logic. The address of a memory location is made available to the processor in the segment:offset format. Before an address is sent to the address bus, it must be translated into an absolute (physical) address. This task is carried out by the address logic unit.

Control unit. The control unit provides the timing and control signals necessary to synchronise the internal operation of the CPU as well as the computer system as a whole.

Basic operation of a microprocessor

A program consists of a sequence of coded instructions which are stored in consequential memory locations. The processor retrieves these instructions one at a time by placing its absolute address on the address bus and enabling the READ control line. The contents of the memory location (the coded instruction) are then placed on the data bus which the processor receives via the data buffers. It is then fed into the instruction unit which decodes the instruction and processes it to the control unit which issues the appropriate timing and control signals for the execution of the instruction.

The coprocessor

The processor carries out mathematical operations using what is known as the floating-point technique. Floating point is a multi-bit representation of large numbers and fractions. The speed of these operations may be vastly improved by the use of a numeric or a maths coprocessor. A maths coprocessor may be a separate stand-alone chip dedicated to performing hardware floating-point mathematical operations or it may be incorporated within the processor chip itself. Recent processors (486 and Pentium) incorporate a built-in floating-point unit (FPU) within the processor chip itself, dispensing with the need for a separate numeric processor. Where individual coprocessor chips are used, they are given the family number 80 x 87, e.g the 80287 and the 80387 to accompany the 80286 and the 80386 processors respectively.

Processing power (MIPS) The performance or processing power of a microprocessor is measured by the number of instructions it carries out per second given in MIPS (Million of Instructions Per Second). The first PC processor, the 8086 launched in 1978, had a power rating of 0.33 MIPS. Five generations later, we have the Pentium with a power rating of 300 MIPS. There are two main factors that determine the MIPS rating of a processor: the processor clock frequency and the time in clock cycles required to execute an instruction. Processor clock frequencies have increased from 5 MHz (8088) to 10 MHz (80286), 25 MHz (80386), 50 MHz (80486) and 100 MHz and over (Pentium). Simultaneously, the time required to execute an instruction has been reduced from an average of 12 cycles per instruction for the 8088/86 to 4.5 cycles for the 80286 and the 80386, 2 cycles for the 80486 and 1 cycle for the Pentium processor. A more practical measure of the relative processing powers of CPUs is the Intel Comparative Microprocessor Performance (ICOMP) which combines the effect of frequency, the number of cycles per instruction, the effect of in-built FPU and on-chip cache memory into a single performance figure. A further method of measuring the performance of a processor was developed by Intel's competitors, AMD and Cyrix. The new rating, known as the P-rating, combines all of the aspects that influence the performance of a PC. It provides a measure of how well the most commonly used applications are run by a PC using a particular processor. This method also provides the most pragmatic rating taking account of all factors that affect processor performance. AMD and Cyrix argue that their processors have a better processing power than comparable Intel products with the same frequency specification. CPU with a P-rating of P-100 indicates that its processing power is equivalent to an Intel running at 100 MHz though it may actually be running at 90 MHz.

Overdrive

Communication between the processor and other units is carried out by a series of high frequency pulses representing the data bits flowing along tightly spaced thin tracks set onto the printed circuit board. High frequency communications present a variety of problems to the designer of a motherboard. Not least is the loss of amplitude, the degradation of the pulse waveform and interference or crosstalk between tracks and devices. Printed circuit boards are designed to avoid signal degradation and high frequency interference. As operating frequencies rise, it becomes more difficult to rely on printed circuit board design to overcome these problems. For this reason, Intel developed the overdrive series of processors. Such processors are identified by the prefix DX2, e.g the 80486DX2.

Computer systems employing this technique double the speed of internal CPU operation while maintaining the system clock frequency. Overdrive processors thus operate on an internal clock frequency which is twice the external system clock. All instructions that can be executed without resort to the system's memory or other devices external to the CPU can be executed at the faster speed. With clock doubling, a processor can double its processing power for operations that fully take place within the chip. However, access to system memory locations and input/output transfers take place at the lower external system clock speed. With a large on-chip cache memory, up to 80 per cent of CPU operations can take place within the chip at the faster speed. Another version of overdrive is the X4 which works on a clock frequency three times the external clock. Other frequency multipliers are also available such as X1.5 and X2.5.

Processor types   Table 6.1 (below) outlines the major properties of the Intel processors.

Second generation, 80286

The second-generation processor, the 80286, was the first processor to break the 1MB barrier. With its 24-bit address, it is capable of addressing 16MB of memory. In addition, it is designed to handle up to 1GB of memory by the use of virtual memory. Virtual memory is secondary memory such as that of a hard disk, the contents of which may be swapped with parts of the directly addressable memory to simulate a larger memory store than 16MB.

Table 6.1

Processor type		Internal data (bits)	External data (bits)	Address bus (bits)	CPU speed (MHz)	Frequency multiplier	Addressable memory	Numeric coprocessor FPU	On-chip cache memory
8088		16	8	20	5	×1	1MB	8087	none
8086		16	16	20	8	×1	1MB	8087	none
80286		16	16	24	10, 12, 16, 20	×1	16MB	80287	none
80386	SX	32	16	24	16 – 25	×1	16MB	80387SX	none
	DX	32	32	32	Up to 40	×1	24MB	80387DX	none
80486	SX	32	16	32	Up to 33	×1	4GB	80486SX	none
	DX	32	32	32	25, 33, 50	×1	4GB	On-chip	L1: 8KB
	DX2	32	32	32	50, 66	×2	4GB	On-chip	L1: 8KB
	DX4	32	32	32	100, 150	×3	4GB	On-chip	L1: 8KB
Pentium		64	32	32	Up to 150	×1, ×1.5 ×2, ×2.5	4GB	On-chip	L1: 16KB
Pentium Pro		32	64	32	Over 150	×2 ×2.5	4GB	On-chip	L1: 16KB L2: 256KB
MMX		32	64	32	Over 150	Varies	4GB	On-chip	L1: 32KB L2: 256KB

Third generation, 80386

The 80386 family contains three offspring. The DX has a data width of 32 bits – hence the D for double word. It was the first Intel processor to enhance its performance by the use of pipelining. Pipelining enables a microprocessor to start executing an instruction before completing the previous one. This is possible because the execution of an instruction generally requires more than one step, each of which may be carried out at different parts of the CPU architecture. Further improvements are obtained by designing the architecture of the processor for the efficient use of pipelining. Such an architecture is known as scalar or superscalar architecture. The 80386 also introduced the virtual real mode operation, commonly known as multi-tasking, in which a number of programs can be loaded and run at the same time using different 1MB slices of extended memory.

The 80386SX offers a cheaper and less powerful version to the 80386DX. It retains its 32-bit internal data width, but has an external data bus of 16 bits only – hence the S for single word. The SX processor thus takes two cycles to load the contents of a memory location into its registers. Its address width remains at 24 bits for 16 MB of directly addressable memory. A low power consumption version is offered by the 80386SL (L for low power) for use in portable or laptop computers.

Fourth generation, 80486

The 80486 processor comes in a number of versions. The DX uses 32 bits for both the internal and external address and data buses. Its performance is further enhanced by an in-built 8KB level 1 (L1) cache memory and an in-built floating-point unit (FPU). It is available in 5 V as well as 3.3 V versions, the latter for use in portable laptop, notebook and other computers where power consumption is of prime consideration. The 80486DX is provided in two versions: DX2 (twice system frequency) and DX4 (three times system frequency).

In the SX version, the in-built numeric coprocessor is removed and the processor maximum clock frequency is reduced. However, it offers a cheaper alternative to the 80486DX for those who have no particular need for a maths processor. A low power version is provided by the 80486SL.

The 80486 incorporates a power-saving technique using an idle mode known as the system management mode (SMM). An extra input control signal (SMI) is introduced which, when enabled, takes the processor into the SMM idle mode. However, before it enters the idle mode, the processor ensures that the contents of its registers are saved in system memory and that all memory operations are completed. Among other things, SMM involves reducing the processor's clock frequency thus reducing its power consumption.

Fifth generation, the Pentium

The Pentium retains the 32-bit data width but doubles its internal data bus to 64 bits which effectively doubles its processing power compared with the 486. The Pentium has an in-built FPU as a standard, two ALU pipelines which allow it to execute two instructions at the same time, a split internal cache memory of 8KB each (one for instructions and the other for data) and an overdrive frequency multiplier of 1, 1.5, 2.0, 2.5 and 3.0. A special cache controller was developed for the Pentium, the 82496, which provides improved performance with an external (L2) cache memory of 256KB or 512KB.

Fifth-generation processors are also available in the x86 architecture manufactured by Cyrix and AMD. The Cyrix 5x86 provides a processor which is compatible with Intel's Pentium with improved P-rating.

Sixth generation, the Pro

Intel calls the sixth-generation processor the Pro; it runs at 150 MHz and offers on-chip 256KB L2 cache memory as well the ordinary Pentium's L1 cache. Placing the L2 cache on the chip itself, rather than on the motherboard, as is the case with the Pentium, enables data to use the internal 64-bit bus thus improving performance. The Pro introduces what is known as dynamic execution which enables the processor to make predictions about the program and execute instructions in advance.

The MMX processor

The MMX is Intel's latest version of the Pentium architecture. It includes a new set of instructions for multimedia functions – hence the name. L1 cache memory is doubled to 32KB which improves its normal performance by 10 per cent. The on-board L2 cache is retained. The benefits of the MMX are realised with new software which makes use of the new MMX instructions. Such applications as communications and graphics, including moving pictures and sound reproduction, are made easier and faster with the new technology. Both AMD and Cyrix have their own version of MMX: the AMD K6 and the Cyrix M2 using different architectural features.

Processor markings

Processor manufacturers stamp each CPU with a mark indicating the type of packaging, the type of processor and the maximum safe speed it can operate at without overheating. A typical marking is

X80486DX4-100

The first letter indicates the type of packaging (in this case X for die), 80486 identifies the type of processor, and DX4 indicates that the maximum motherboard speed is one-third of the processor's speed, namely 33 MHz, and -100 specifies the maximum safe speed of the processor, namely 100 MHz. If higher speeds are used, the processor will get excessively hot and its life span will be short. Other markings may include the maximum temperature, the operating voltage and the type of integrated on-board cache. For instance,

A80486DX2-80 N V 8 T

where A specifies that the package is a ceramic pin grid array, 80486 is the processor type, DX2 is the multiplier, -80 is the speed in MHz, N is a micro code, V indicates 3.3 V d.c. supply requirement, 8 indicates 8 KB cache and T indicates a write-through cache.

Processor packaging

First-generation processors, the 8088/86, were packaged into the traditional DIL rectangular containers (Fig. 6.2). More than 40 pins are required with pin number 1 identified by the special mark shown. Modern processor packages are compact squares which avoid long signal paths and provide a larger number of pins. The most common package is the pin grid array (PGA) illustrated in Fig. 6.3. The pins are arranged in two rows for 16-bit processors, three rows for 32-bit processors, while the Pentium requires four rows. Pin 1 is identified by having the corner of the case where it is located chopped off as shown. The processor is inserted into a chip carrier or socket which is soldered to the motherboard (Fig. 6.4). Modern systems use a zero insertion force (ZIF) socket which has a lever that can release the grip of the socket on the processor pins (Fig. 6.5).

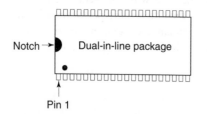

Notch → Dual-in-line package

Pin 1

Figure 6.2 The DIL processor IC package

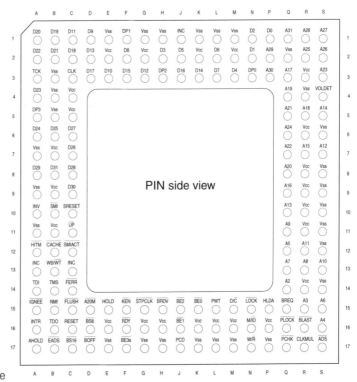

Figure 6.3   Pin-grid-array (PGA) package

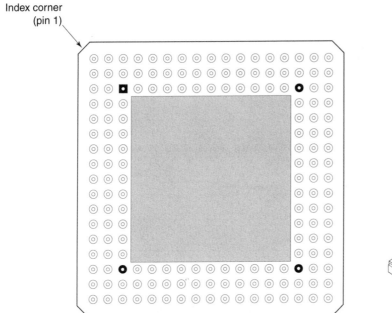

Figure 6.4   PGA carrier or socket

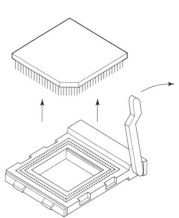

Figure 6.5   The zero-insertion force CPU socket

Other IC packages include the leadless chip carrier (LCC) with plastic pads in place of the pins, and the more popular plastic quad flat package (PQFP) (or simply plastic flat pack, PFP) which are designed to be soldered on the board (Fig. 6.6).

Heat sink

Processors such as the 80486DX range and the Pentium produce a large amount of heat which has to be dissipated using heat sinks. The simplest heat sink is a suitably shaped heat-conducting piece of metal (usually aluminium) that is clipped or glued to the processor. It acts like a radiator taking the heat away from the chip. Further cooling may be produced using a small electric fan placed above the processor and driven from a 12 V d.c. line from the power supply.

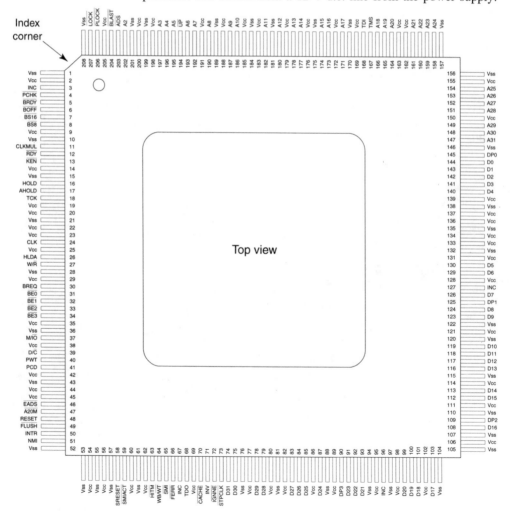

Figure 6.6 The plastic quad flat package (PQFP)

7 The expansion bus

An expansion bus is more than a simple electric conductor. A PC expansion bus must be able to transfer data across its contacts flawlessly without degradation in amplitude, frequency or pulse shape. Data must also be transferred according to a strict timing sequence. For this reason, extra signals are included to control the flow of information, its speed and bit pattern.

The original XT motherboard provided the first expansion slot, the ISA (Industry Standard Architecture). The ISA bus was designed to operate at a speed comparable with the 8088/86 processors. In essence, the ISA bus was an extension of the CPU bus itself with additional control signals. However, as faster processors were manufactured, wait states had to be introduced to slow the processor every time it accessed memory locations via the slower bus. These slow bus architectures formed a separate bus structure usually known as the system bus. Furthermore, the demand for backward compatibility ensured the continued use of the slow ISA expansion bus in 486 and Pentium-based motherboards.

There are five main expansion bus architectures offered by compatible PCs: ISA, EISA, MCA, VESA local bus and PCI.

The ISA bus

The ISA is the original and still the most widely used expansion bus. The first ISA slot, a 62-way double-sided slot (the XT bus), provided access to 8-bit data, a 20-bit address and most of the control lines. For a 16-bit system, a second, 36-way extension connector is added to provide access to the remaining 8 bits of data as well as other lines as shown in Fig. 7.1.

The pin-out of an ISA bus is shown in Fig. 7.2. Of the 62 contacts used for XT 8-bit expansion cards (A1–A31 and B1–B31), 20 are address lines, eight are data lines, three are grounds and five are d.c. supply (two 5 V, and one each for −5 V, +12 V and −12 V). The bus supports six interrupts (IRQ3, 4, 5, 6, 7 and 9) and three DMA channels. The XT bus runs at a speed of 4.77 MHz provided at clock

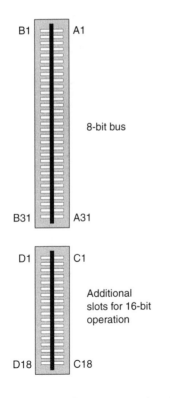

B1　A1

8-bit bus

B31　A31

D1　C1

Additional slots for 16-bit operation

D18　C18

Figure 7.1　ISA bus expansion slot

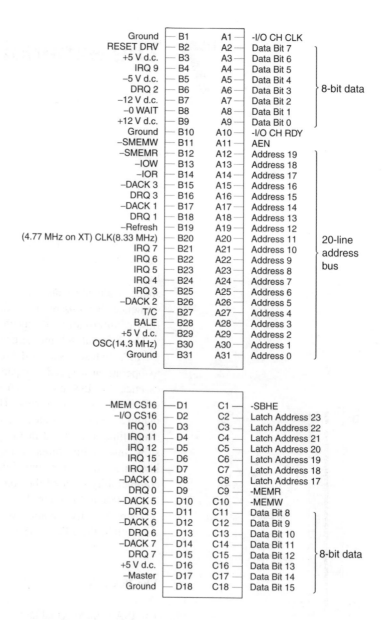

Ground	B1	A1	-I/O CH CLK
RESET DRV	B2	A2	Data Bit 7
+5 V d.c.	B3	A3	Data Bit 6
IRQ 9	B4	A4	Data Bit 5
–5 V d.c.	B5	A5	Data Bit 4
DRQ 2	B6	A6	Data Bit 3
–12 V d.c.	B7	A7	Data Bit 2
–0 WAIT	B8	A8	Data Bit 1
+12 V d.c.	B9	A9	Data Bit 0
Ground	B10	A10	-I/O CH RDY
–SMEMW	B11	A11	AEN
–SMEMR	B12	A12	Address 19
–IOW	B13	A13	Address 18
–IOR	B14	A14	Address 17
–DACK 3	B15	A15	Address 16
DRQ 3	B16	A16	Address 15
–DACK 1	B17	A17	Address 14
DRQ 1	B18	A18	Address 13
–Refresh	B19	A19	Address 12
(4.77 MHz on XT) CLK(8.33 MHz)	B20	A20	Address 11
IRQ 7	B21	A21	Address 10
IRQ 6	B22	A22	Address 9
IRQ 5	B23	A23	Address 8
IRQ 4	B24	A24	Address 7
IRQ 3	B25	A25	Address 6
–DACK 2	B26	A26	Address 5
T/C	B27	A27	Address 4
BALE	B28	A28	Address 3
+5 V d.c.	B29	A29	Address 2
OSC(14.3 MHz)	B30	A30	Address 1
Ground	B31	A31	Address 0

8-bit data (spanning A2–A9)

20-line address bus (spanning A12–A31)

–MEM CS16	D1	C1	-SBHE
–I/O CS16	D2	C2	Latch Address 23
IRQ 10	D3	C3	Latch Address 22
IRQ 11	D4	C4	Latch Address 21
IRQ 12	D5	C5	Latch Address 20
IRQ 15	D6	C6	Latch Address 19
IRQ 14	D7	C7	Latch Address 18
–DACK 0	D8	C8	Latch Address 17
DRQ 0	D9	C9	-MEMR
–DACK 5	D10	C10	-MEMW
DRQ 5	D11	C11	Data Bit 8
–DACK 6	D12	C12	Data Bit 9
DRQ 6	D13	C13	Data Bit 10
–DACK 7	D14	C14	Data Bit 11
DRQ 7	D15	C15	Data Bit 12
+5 V d.c.	D16	C16	Data Bit 13
–Master	D17	C17	Data Bit 14
Ground	D18	C18	Data Bit 15

8-bit data (spanning C11–C18)

Figure 7.2 ISA pin-out

pin B20. The oscillator pin B30 provides the 14.3 MHz system oscillator signal.

The 36-way extension bus (C1–C18 and D1–D31) provides an extra 8 bits of data and four more address lines together with five more interrupts (IRQ10-IRQ14) and four more DMA channels. The bus speed is increased to 8.33 MHz (pin B20) replacing the XT 4.77 MHz clock.

Data throughput An important property of an expansion bus is what is known as its data throughput given in million bits per second, Mbits/s. Data throughput is the rate of transfer of a standard unit of 8-bit data. For instance, the XT 8-bit ISA operating at a frequency of 4.77 MHz has a throughput of

4.77 MHz $\times$ 8 bits/8 bits = 4.77 Mbits/s

Similarly, the 16-bit ISA operating at a frequency of 8.33 MHz has a data throughput of

8.33 $\times$ 16/8 = 16.66 Mbits/s

The EISA bus   The EISA (Extended Industry Standard Architecture) is another 32-bit bus based on the original ISA bus. The additional bits are accommodated by a second layer of contacts. ISA cards make contact with the upper level only, whilst 32-bit cards make contact with both layers. In this way, backward compatibility with the ISA system is maintained. The EISA bus provides access to 15 interrupt levels and seven DMA channels and runs at the same speed as the ISA bus, namely 8.33 MHz. However, because it has double the data width, its potential data throughput is twice that of the ISA bus, namely 32.32 Mbits/s. Like the MCA bus, EISA uses hardware arbitration and bus mastering techniques to allow other processors or devices to gain control of the bus.

The MCA bus   The MCA (Micro Channel Architecture) is a 178-way expansion bus designed to meet the requirements of the 80386 processor both in terms of data width and speed. The MCA bus has a clock frequency of 10 MHz, a 32-bit data bus and 32 address lines. The connector is divided into three main segments, 8-bit, 16-bit and 32-bit segments, as shown in Fig. 7.3. A video extension is provided by a special 8-bit segment (AV1–AV10 and BV1–BV10).

The MCA provides a data throughput which is more than double that of the 16-bit ISA:

MCA throughput = 10 MHz $\times$ 32/8 = 40 Mbits/s

The most important aspect of the MCA is the use of a hardware arbitration system which has been copied in all subsequent bus architectures. Unlike the ISA, where the CPU keeps control of the bus at all times, with the MCA system control of the bus is shared

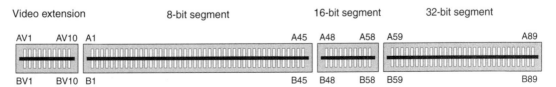

Figure 7.3   MCA expansion slot

between a number of devices known as bus masters. A bus master is an adaptor with its own subprocessor that can execute operations independently of the CPU. Arbitration and bus mastering require a bus controller chip and a number of new control lines (arbitration and arbitration/grant lines) to be included on the bus.

MCA is incompatible with any other bus system and requires special circuitry that must be included in all cards and adaptors. For this reason, MCA failed to gain popularity and very few computer manufacturers offer it on their motherboards.

The VESA local bus (VL-Bus)

The VESA (Video Electronics Standards Association) local bus, often known as the VL-Bus, is a truly local bus originally designed to be used for video cards. It offers direct access to the system memory at the speed of the processor itself. It can move 32 bits of data all at one time, between the CPU and video and other subsystems such as a hard disk. The VL-Bus is designed to augment existing expansion bus systems. It was positioned as an extension of ISA, EISA or MCA slots. Fig. 7.4 shows a VESA local bus arrangement with ISA slots. VL-Bus release 2.0 offers an extension for 64-bit operation with a potential throughput of 260 Mbits/s.

Despite its obvious advantages, the VESA local bus suffers from a number of serious drawbacks including a practical speed limitation of 33 MHz, 486 processor dependency and a practical constraint on the number of slots that may be made available.

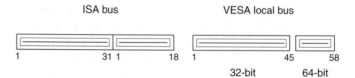

Figure 7.4 The VESA local bus slot

The PCI bus

The PCI (Peripheral Component Interface) is designed to work at the full clock speed of Intel processors. Because of such high speeds, the physical positioning of the chips in relation to the 'PCI speedway' becomes critical. As a result, PCI specifications include the physical configuration of the motherboard itself.

The PCI bus comes in two versions: a 32-bit version (124-way) and a 64-bit version (188-way) as shown in Fig. 7.5. It supports a clock frequency of 33 MHz giving a throughput of 132 Mbits/s and 264 Mbits/s for 32-bit and 64-bit operations respectively. PCI uses such techniques as linear burst for fast data transfer and concurrency

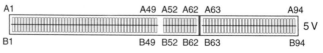

Figure 7.5 The PCI expansion bus slot

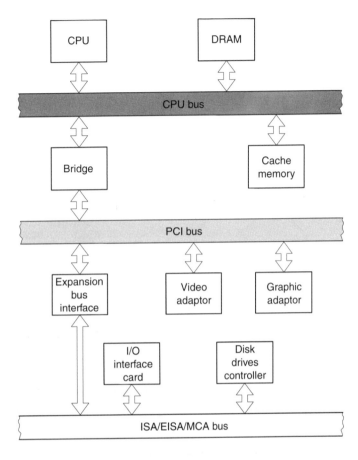

Figure 7.6 PC bus hierarchy

in which the CPU can operate simultaneously with other bus masters. Although the PCI bus is sometimes described as a local bus, it is one step removed from a truly local bus. As can be seen from Fig. 7.6, the PCI architecture creates an intermediary bus, known as the 'PCI local bus', between the CPU local bus and the traditional I/O expansion bus. Hence, the PCI bus is often referred to as a mezzanine bus. Cache and main DRAM memory is served directly by the CPU local bus; the PCI bus serves options that require fast memory transfer (video, graphics and audio sound). Other peripherals are served by the standard ISA, EISA or MCA buses. Data transfer between the CPU local bus and the PCI bus is controlled by a bridge interface and, similarly, a bus expansion interface controls data transfer from the PCI bus to the other standard bus slots.

The PC Card (PCMCIA) The development of expansion cards for portable (laptop or notebook) computers followed a general standard, namely the PC Card developed by the Personal Computer Memory Card Industry Association (PCMCIA). The PC Card is a credit-card-sized

Figure 7.7 The PCMCIA card connector

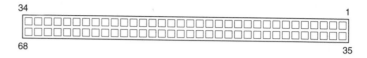

expansion board that slots into a small 68-way edge connector provided on portable computers (Fig. 7.7). It can provide memory expansion units, tiny hard drives, modems, sound, CD-ROM controllers and a host of other peripherals. The PC Card system is self-configuring, dispensing with the need for jumper/DIP switch settings. The card contains all the necessary information for the host computer to set it up, assign memory space for it and communicate with it. This is carried out by a software interface called Socket Services, which provides the underlying basic input/output routines necessary to access the card's hardware, something akin to BIOS for the host computer. There are four PCMCIA standards, Types I to IV, which among other things differ in thickness.

Riser slots

The number and types of expansion slots vary among computers. Most PCs offer eight expansion slots of one or more types. To save space on the board, a single expansion slot may be soldered onto the motherboard into which a riser card is slotted. The riser card offers a number of expansion slots on its sides. Adaptor cards may then be installed into the riser card to get access to the expansion bus.

Expansion bus comparison

The following table gives a comparison of expansion buses.

Type	Data bits	Speed (MHz)	Comment
ISA	8/16	8.33	Extensively used
EISA	32	8.33	Two-level contacts; failed to gain general acceptance
MCA	32	10.00	Failed to gain general acceptance
VESA	32/64	33	Used mainly for fast video graphics; cannot be used on 64-bit systems
PCI	32/64	33	Processor independent; may prove to be market leader
PCMCIA	16	Varies	PC Cards for laptop and notebook computers

8 The booting-up process

The purpose of a PC is to load and run application software such as word processing, computer-aided engineering, Windows or games packages. An application package is designed for a specific operating system such as MS-DOS, PS/2, UNIX or Windows 95. The operating system provides an environment for different software packages to be installed and run. The link between the operating system and the hardware components of the PC is provided by BIOS (Basic Input/Output System). BIOS is a set of short routines which are stored in a ROM or an EPROM device – hence the name ROM BIOS.

The functions of BIOS

BIOS routines are stored in a ROM or EPROM chip with memory addresses located in the upper segment of real memory. The number and size of BIOS depend on the manufacturer of the chip and its version, with later versions containing more complex and sophisticated programs. BIOS routines may be divided into two categories:

1. Start-up routines.
2. Basic low level input/output routines.

The start-up routines are initiated when the system is switched on (cold start) or has been reset (warm start). They include such programs as the initial power on self-test (POST) and system initialisation.

The I/O routines, which include such programs as print routines and disk read/write, are called when the operating system or an application package wishes to carry out these basic tasks. This simplifies application program writing and helps to ensure compatibility of PCs which have different hardware elements or configurations. Access to these routines is provided by a system of software interrupts which cause the processor to halt its operation and start a particular BIOS routine. Each interrupt is given a 4-byte value known as a vector which acts as a pointer to the required routine. Each vector is allocated four memory locations into which BIOS loads the 4-byte value during the start-up routine. Interrupt vectors are collected into a table, known as an interrupt vector table, which is located in memory locations at the very start of system RAM, beginning at address 0000:0000.

The boot-up process

When a computer system is switched on, a procedure known as boot-up or start-up is initiated by the CPU which among other things runs BIOS and loads the operating system to get the computer ready for use.

Upon power-up (by turning the mains switch on), the power supply performs a self-test procedure which, if successful and the correct voltages are established on its output lines, sends a power good (PG) signal to the timer chip on the motherboard. The timer responds by taking the reset control line HIGH to start up the CPU. The following is the sequence of events that will take place in a typical computer system:

Step 1. *Bootstrap.* The CPU searches for starting address FFFF:0000 where the first instruction is stored. This instruction, which is a jump instruction, directs the processor to the starting address where BIOS is located. This step is traditionally known as the bootstrap after the notion of the PC 'pulling itself up by its bootstraps'.

Step 2. *POST.* The first action of BIOS is to test the system, a routine known as POST (Power On Self-Test).

Step 3. *Initialisation.* Following a successful self-test, BIOS carries out a system initialising routine.

Step 4. *Loading the operating system.* This involves the BIOS looking for, loading and executing two hidden system files: IO.SYS and MSDOS.SYS.

The computer is now under the control of the operating system in the guise of IO.SYS.

Step 5. *Loading CONFIG.SYS and COMMAND.COM.* The operating system takes action to establish the operating environment of the system as specified by the user. Customising the environment involves, in the first instance, searching the root directory for a file called CONFIG.SYS. If one is found, DOS reads and executes all its statements before loading the DOS kernel, a file called COMMAND.COM. If CONFIG.SYS cannot be found, COMMAND.COM is loaded regardless.

The system is now under the control of COMMAND.COM.

Step 6.   *Loading AUTOEXEC.BAT.* The CPU looks for a batch file called AUTOEXEC.BAT. If it is present, DOS loads it into memory, executes its commands and displays the DOS prompt. If AUTOEXEC.BAT is not present, DOS will request DATE and TIME, before displaying the DOS prompt.

The system is now ready for DOS commands or application programs.

Power on self-test (POST)   POST starts with a series of tests known as the core tests of the motherboard hardware including the processor, the coprocessor, the timer and interval chip and the DMA and interrupt controllers. If an error is detected, coded beeps are produced. The exact code varies according to the BIOS manufacturer. The video adaptor is tested next. If the test is successful, a cursor appears on the screen. If the test fails, depending on the nature of the error, a message may appears along the lines of 'video ROM error'.

The second series of tests involve testing system memory, i.e. RAM and ROM devices, the floppy and hard disk drives, the serial and parallel (printer) ports and the keyboard. These test involve a BIOS routine which sends data to memory locations, registers or port addresses and testing the result by reading back the contents of these locations. For ROM devices a checksum test is performed where the contents of ROM locations are read and a CRC (Cyclic Redundancy Count) sum, known as a checksum, is produced and checked against a known-good count. Errors are reported by audible coded beeps or displayed as messages or both.

This second set of tests is skipped if the boot-up process was a result of a 'warm' start, i.e. a result of pressing the reset button. 'Warm' or 'cold' starts are indicated by the contents of memory location 0000:0472 which the CPU reads before initiating these tests. A reading of 1234 (HEX) indicates a 'warm' start, otherwise a cold start is assumed.

Upon the successful completion of both sets of tests, a single short beep is produced.

Initialising the system   The second task of BIOS is to execute initialisation routines that recognise and configure various parts of the system. BIOS searches through the system and identifies its various features such as the number and types of ports installed and the type of display adaptor (monochrome or colour). Initialisation involves creating an interrupt vector table, loading specified memory locations and registers with appropriate data (such as keyboard character style and start addresses of installed I/O adaptors) to reflect the specific features of the system. This information is stored in what is known as the

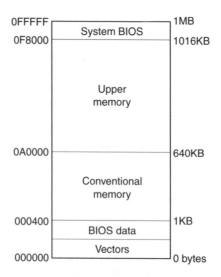

Figure 8.1 PC memory map showing the BIOS data space

BIOS data area which comprises 256 bytes of memory starting at address location 0000:0400 (absolute address 00040) as shown in Fig. 8.1.

CMOS set-up

In the process of testing and initialising the system, BIOS needs to know the number and type of peripherals that are installed and the size of memory that has to be tested. BIOS can be programmed to find this information by itself. However, this will take time as BIOS carries out a lengthy search. To avoid such delay on booting up, all PCs record this vital information in a non-volatile RAM. A battery-backed CMOS RAM device, a Motorola MC146818, known as a CMOS set-up chip, is used for that purpose. A total of 64 bytes are made available to store set-up information such as date and time, number and types of disk drives installed, cache memory, etc. CMOS set-up may be accessed by pressing one key or a combination of keys during the boot-up process.

Looking for the operating system

So far, the process of initialising the system has been non-operating system specific. Any operating system may now be loaded and BIOS will seek to find an operating system and load it. The operating system is usually contained in the hard disk drive C:. An operating system may also be available on a floppy disk, known as a system or boot disk, in which case the boot disk must be inserted in drive A:.

An operating system is identified by a signature on the boot sector of the disk indicating the presence of system files located on the outside track (track 0) of the disk. The name and number of the system files depends on the operating system used. MS-DOS uses two system files: IO.SYS (or IBMBIO.SYS) and MSDOS.SYS (or IBMDOS.SYS).

The process of looking for the operating system involves BIOS first interrogating the A: drive for the presence of an operating system followed by the C: hard drive. This 'C:, A:' sequence, known as the boot-up sequence, may be changed by the CMOS set-up. If a non-system disk, one without the correct boot signature, is detected in A:, the following message is displayed:

```
Non-system disk or disk error
Replace and strike any key when ready
```

If the system files are missing from the disk, the following message will be displayed:

```
Missing operating system
```

The system files are given three attributes: S (for system), H (for hidden) and R (for read-only). The R and S attributes protect the files against deletion by mistake. The H attribute ensures that they are not included in the DIR listing. For hidden files to be listed, a switch /a (for attributes) or /h (for hidden) has to be used. A typical DIR /a listing for MS-DOS is shown in Fig. 8.2. It should be noticed that the system files are the first two entries in the directory. This used to be an essential requirement for DOS versions 3.3 or earlier.

```
SHR   C:\IO.SYS
SHR   C:\MSDOS.SYS
  R   C:\COMMAND.COM
SHR   C:\DBLSPACE.BIN
A     C:\WINA20.386
A     C:\CONFIG.OLD
A     C:\AUTOEXEC.OLD
A     C:\CONFIG.SYS
```

Figure 8.2 A typical DIR /a display

Loading the operating system

Once the system files have been located, they are loaded into system memory, read and executed. IO.SYS is loaded and executed first followed by MSDOS.SYS. The system files contain all the necessary information to set up the system, its components and subsystems. This includes resetting the disk drives, initialising the printer and the parallel and serial ports and setting up the system's default parameters.

Configuring the system – CONFIG.SYS

Following the execution of the system files, DOS looks for the system configuration file, CONFIG.SYS, in the root directory of drive C: (or drive A: in the case of booting up from A:), loads it, reads it several times and executes its instructions. Next, DOS looks for a file called COMMAND.COM in root directory C: (or A: in the case of booting up from A:) and loads it in low memory. COMMAND.COM, which is usually given an R (read-only) attribute, contains DOS's resident (internal) commands.

The purpose of CONFIG.SYS is to configure and install hardware devices and load their respective control programs known as device drivers. Invariably, CONFIG.SYS has to be modified whenever a new option is added to the system. A faulty command statement in

CONFIG.SYS is usually indicated on the display. Some errors may cause the boot-up process to be halted.

Customising the system with AUTOEXEC.BAT

Before the DOS prompt appears on the screen, DOS (and Windows 95) looks into root directory C: (or A: in the case of booting up from A:) for a batch file called AUTOEXEC.BAT and executes its commands. AUTOEXEC.BAT may contain command lines which determine the type of prompt, set a path or configure the keyboard character set.

A faulty command line in AUTOEXEC.BAT is usually indicated on the display. Some errors may cause the boot-up process to be halted.

Bypassing CONFIG.SYS and AUTOEXEC.BAT

In cases where booting up of the system is halted owing to errors in CONFIG.SYS or AUTOEXEC.BAT, DOS provides a facility for bypassing both files. The two files may be completely bypassed by pressing F8 at the point when BIOS begins to load MS-DOS. A message to the effect that CONFIG.SYS and AUTOEXEC.BAT have been bypassed will be displayed.

Another facility which prompts the user to step through CONFIG.SYS and AUTOEXEC.BAT is provided by pressing F5 at the point when MS-DOS begins to be loaded.

Path to DOS files

DOS's internal or resident commands which are built into COMMAND.COM are loaded into system RAM at the boot-up stage. The external or transient commands remain on the disk in the form of individual files which are usually placed in a special subdirectory called DOS. For this reason a path has to be established to ensure that external commands may be called without having to change directories.

CONFIG.SYS commands

The following are some of the main DOS commands that are valid for CONFIG.SYS files:

BREAK ON Instructs DOS to check for Ctrl+C or Ctrl+Break key combinations, which if pressed causes the program to be halted.

OFF DOS does not check for a key combination.

Example: BREAK ON

BUFFERS Sets the amount of memory used as buffers for data transfer. When data is transferred between, say, a hard disk and another unit, data is first stored in a number of buffers before it is sent to its intended destination.

A small number of buffers can reduce the speed

	of data transfer. However, a large number of buffers will reduce the size of conventional memory. With each buffer occupying 512 bytes of memory, a typical number of buffers is between 20 and 40.
Example:	BUFFERS=30
FILES	Determines the number of files DOS can keep open at the same time.
Example:	FILES=20
COUNTRY	Sets the keyboard characters to a particular country style. The character set for each country is available in a file called COUNTRY.SYS located in the DOS subdirectory. The default is US-style characters which are the same as those used in the UK.
Example:	COUNTRY=044,,C:\DOS\COUNTRY.SYS where '044' is the code for English (UK) based on the international telephone code, and 'C:\DOS\ COUNTRY.SYS' is the path to the relevant file.
DEVICE	Sets and loads the routine that controls an installed hardware device called the device driver. This command installs the device driver into conventional memory. If the installed device is a mouse, then a routine that controls the mouse, typically MOUSE.SYS or IMOUSE.SYS, has to be loaded by a device statement which merely states the path to the relevant file.
Examples:	DEVICE=C:\MOUSE\MOUSE.SYS MOUSE.SYS is the mouse driver stored in subdirectory MOUSE.
	DEVICE=C:\DOS\HIMEM.SYS which enables high memory management routine, HIMEM.SYS.
	DEVICE=C:\DOS\EMM386.EXE NOEMS which provides access to upper memory without creating expanded memory.
DEVICEHIGH	This has the same effect as the DEVICE command except that it loads the device driver into the upper memory area.
Example:	DEVICEHIGH=C:\MOUSE\MOUSE.SYS
DOS	When set HIGH, it loads the DOS kernel, COMMAND.COM, into the upper memory area, UMA.
Example:	DOS=HIGH

	When set to UMB, it creates upper memory blocks which allow TSRs to be loaded into upper memory.

Example: DOS=UMB or DOS=HIGH, UMB

LASTDRIVE Specifies the highest drive letter.
Example: LASTDRIVE=K
which provides a maximum of 11 disk drives, A: to K:.

NUMBLOCK ON   Sets the Num Lock of the numeric keypad on.
OFF   Sets the Num Lock of the numeric keypad off.

REM Indicates that the text that follows is a descriptive remark and should be bypassed. It is also used to disable a command line without deleting it.
Example: REM DEVICEHIGH=C:\MOUSE\MOUSE.SYS
to disable the mouse driver command line.

The order of these commands appearing in CONFIG.SYS is unimportant with the exception that DEVICE commands must come before DEVICEHIGH commands.

AUTOEXEC.BAT files   AUTOEXEC.BAT is a batch file which DOS executes at the boot-up stage to customise the PC. It consists of a series of commands which DOS carries out in the sequence they are written. These instructions include DOS batch commands such as ECHO, PATH and PROMPT. It may also contain instructions to load TSR programs such as DOSKEY which memorises and reproduces previous commands.

Typical AUTOEXEC.BAT commands

ECHO ON To display the command lines as they are executed by DOS.
ECHO OFF Not to display the command lines as they are executed by DOS.
@ECHO OFF Not to display any command lines including ECHO OFF itself.

PROMPT To set the type of prompt.
Examples: PROMPT PG
in which $P displays the directory path (e.g. C:\ or A:\ or C:\DOS\) and $G displays the greater than, >, sign.
PROMPT $D
to display the current date.

PATH To specify the directories and subdirectories that should be searched by DOS when looking for a filename. When instructed to execute a command, DOS first searches system memory for a resident command file. If it fails to locate the file there, it searches the current root directory, followed by any other directory specified in a PATH command.

Examples: PATH=C:\; C:\DOS
to search root directory C:\ and subdirectory C:\DOS.

PATH=C:\DOS;C:\WINDOWS
to search subdirectories DOS and WINDOWS. Root directory C:\ is automatically searched.

KEYB To configure the keyboard for a specific language.
Example: KEYB UK,,C:\DOS\KEYBOARD.SYS
to specify the keyboard to English (UK). The default setting is English (USA).

SET This command sets, i.e. defines, what is known as an environment variable. For instance, some programs require a temporary directory, usually called TEMP or TMP, into which temporary files are stored. Such a directory can be defined by the command SET.

Example: SET TEMP=C:\
to define the TEMP directory in root directory C:\. To call this directory, the programmer writes '%TEMP%' which will be substituted with C:\.

CD To change the active directory.
Example: CD WINDOWS
to change to subdirectory WINDOWS, in which case the prompt will be C:\WINDOWS\>.

AUTOEXEC.BAT may also be used to launch an application program at the boot-up stage. For instance, to run WINDOWS immediately upon booting up, the following line should be included:

```
CD WINDOWS
WIN
```

The first line changes the active directory to WINDOWS and the second line is the filename to run WINDOWS. The first line may be dispensed with if the PATH command line included a path to WINDOWS.

Basic elements of a CONFIG.SYS file

```
DEVICE = C:\MOUSE\MOUSE.SYS
DEVICE = C:\DOS\HIMEM.SYS
```

```
DEVICE = C:\DOS\EMM386.EXE NOEMS
DOS = HIGH, UMB
COUNTRY = 044,,C:\DOS\COUNTRY.SYS
FILES = 40
BUFFERS = 20
LASTDRIVE = Z
```

Basic elements of an AUTOEXEC.BAT file

```
@ECHO OFF
PROMPT $P$G
PATH C:\WINDOWS; C:\DOS
SET TEMP = C:\DOS
KEYB UK,,C:\DOS\KEYBOARD.SYS
```

The system or boot disk

A system disk, also known as a boot disk, is a floppy which may be inserted in drive A: to start up the computer. It contains what is known as the system, i.e. the system files IO.SYS and MSDOS.SYS, and the DOS kernel, COMMAND.COM. Creating a system disk involves 'transferring the system' from drive C: onto a target disk in drive A: (or B:). There are two commands that may be used to transfer the system:

SYS A:
FORMAT A: /s (switch /s stands for system)

Both methods will copy the system files and COMMAND.COM together with their attributes. However, formatting a disk as a system disk will wipe the disk clean, thus losing all existing files.

Depending on the version of DOS, a system disk may include one or more additional system files such as DRVSPACE.BIN with SHR attributes. Furthermore, it is usual to have a number of non-resident DOS files on the system floppy disk, such as EDIT.EXE, QBASIC.EXE, FORMAT.COM, FDISK.EXE and MSD.EXE, to provide access to some useful external commands.

Installing the operating system

The operating system is usually installed on the hard disk drive C: and is provided on a number of disks which contain all operating system files as well as an install or set-up routine. The operating system may be installed by inserting disk 1 in drive A: and running the set-up program (by typing SETUP at the prompt). The set-up program will take all necessary steps including writing CONFIG.SYS and AUTOEXEC.BAT files and creating subdirectories to install the operating system fully.

In the absence of a complete set of operating system disks, the operating system may be installed 'manually'. This involves three steps:

Step 1. Transferring 'the system' from a system floppy disk inserted in drive A: onto the hard disk. Both SYS C: and FORMAT C:/s may be used. However, since formatting a disk wipes out all of the files on the disk, SYS C: is usually used.

Step 2. Creating a subdirectory, normally called DOS, into which all non-resident files are to be copied.

Step 3. Constructing appropriate CONFIG.SYS and AUTOEXEC.BAT files and saving them into root directory C:\. It is normal to make a copy of these two files under different names, e.g. CONFIG.OLD and AUTOEXEC.OLD.

Making more memory available

The amount of conventional memory available for use by a computer affects the programs it can run and how fast they run. Making more memory available takes several forms:

1. Deleting unnecessary files which makes more conventional memory available.

2. Loading MS-DOS into high memory area also saves conventional memory. This is carried out by including DOS=HIGH in CONFIG.SYS.

3. Using memory management routines. There are two such routines: HIMEM.SYS and EMM386.exe.

    HIMEM.SYS manages the use of extended memory and provides the first chain for DOS to use the upper memory area.

    EMM386.EXE provides access to the upper memory area into which device drivers may be re-located from conventional memory. It also simulates expanded memory by allocating a section of extended memory for expanded memory applications.

    e.g. DEVICE=C:\DOS\EMM386.EXE NOEMS
    or   DEVICE=C:\DOS\EMM386.EXE RAM

    EMM386.EXE works in conjunction with HIMEM.SYS and must be entered into CONFIG.SYS after HIMMEM.SYS. A typical entry in CONFIG.SYS is

    DEVICE = C:\DOS\HIMEM.SYS
    DEVICE = C:\DOS\EMM386.EXE

    When expanded memory is not required, NOEMS is added to the command line. Conversely, RAM is added to the driver for expanded memory operation.

4. Relocating TSRs and device drivers from conventional memory to upper memory. For this to take place, a further command line in CONFIG.SYS is necessary, namely

    DOS = UMB

Relocation is carried out by the DEVICEHIGH command in CONFIG.SYS and LOADHIGH (LH) in AUTOEXEC.BAT. The number of relocations that are possible depends on the size of the programs and the free space in upper memory. Optimum relocation is achieved with the larger programs located in the larger spaces in upper memory.

Optimum memory saving may be obtained by DOS's MEMMAKER routine. MEMMAKER modifies CONFIG.SYS and AUTOEXEC.BAT files so that device drivers and other memory-resident programs use less conventional memory. MEMMAKER examines the installed programs and by trial and error finds the best possible fit into upper memory for optimum size of conventional memory.

9 Interrupts

The most distinguishing feature of a PC is its ability to respond to a number of different requests for service that come from a software program or a hardware unit. This is made possible by the CPU's interrupt procedure in which the processor suspends its main program and transfers its attention to perform a particular service such as displaying a character following a keystroke or sending data to a printer. These services are performed by running a program known as a handler routine (Fig. 9.1).

Processing an interrupt

Compatible PCs support 256 different interrupts numbered INT0 to INT255 (or INT00H to INTFFH, H for HEX). A number of interrupts are allocated specific tasks, such as INT09H for keyboard service or INT13H for disk drive I/O. The allocation of these tasks is carried out at the boot-up stage by the BIOS program.

When an interrupt is received, the processor takes the following steps:

1. It completes its current instruction and suspends the main program.
2. It loads the contents of its internal registers into a section of memory known as the stack.
3. It performs the task or procedure requested by the interrupt command by locating and running the particular interrupt service routine (ISR) known as the interrupt handler.

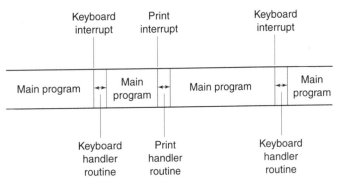

Figure 9.1

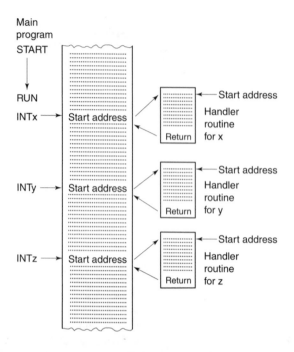

Figure 9.2

4. When the handler program is completed, the processor reloads the registers with their original contents from the stack and resumes the main program.

The handler routine is located in a sequence of system memory locations and is identified by the 4-byte (32-bit) address of the first location (the start address) where the program is stored, as shown in Fig. 9.2. The start addresses of all available handler routines are stored in groups of four consecutive 8-bit memory locations as shown in Fig. 9.3. The first 1KB of computer memory (0000:0000 to 0000:03FF) is used for storing the start addresses with the first 2 bytes of each group specifying the offset whilst the second 2 bytes specify the segment of the handler's starting address. The address where the first byte of the start address is located is known as the interrupt vector. INT00H thus has a vector of 0000 and INT0CH has a vector of 0030. In effect, the interrupt vector = 4 × the INT number, as illustrated in Fig. 9.3. For instance, INT0B has an interrupt vector of 4 × 0B = 002C. This list of all 256 interrupts and their vectors is known as the interrupt vector table. The loading of start addresses of interrupt handlers into their appropriate vector locations is carried out by the BIOS program at the boot-up stage.

When an interrupt is called, the processor looks for the interrupt vector number in the interrupt vector table which lists all of the 256 interrupts and their respective vectors. Once the vector number is identified and with it the location where the first byte of the handler routine is stored, the CPU goes to that location and retrieves the handler starting address. The handler routine is then run.

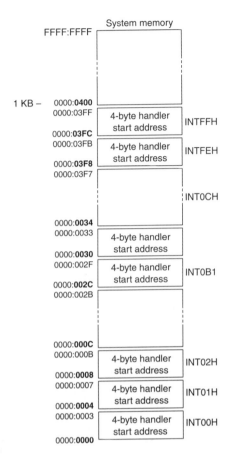

Figure 9.3 Interrupts and their vectors

Software and hardware interrupts

Interrupts are generally divided into two types: software or internal (also known as an exception) and hardware or external. Software interrupts are special instructions that may arise as a result of the processor detecting a fault, e.g. a floating-point error, or they may be triggered as part of a software program. Hardware interrupt are invoked by a peripheral device or unit taking the interrupt request (INTR) input of the processor LOW. The processor also has a special interrupt input known as non-maskable interrupt (NMI) which, once invoked, must be immediately processed by the CPU.

Hardware interrupt request (INTR)

A processor has a single INTR control line which has to be shared by all peripherals and devices such as the keyboard, disk drive, serial and parallel ports, system timer and real-time clock (RTC). Each such device generates an individual hardware interrupt request (IRQ) signal. The original XT computer provided eight hardware interrupts numbered IRQ0 to IRQ7. This was extended to 16 (IRQ0 to IRQ15) with the introduction of the AT compatible PC. Each hardware

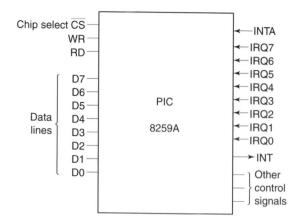

Figure 9.4 The 8259A programmable interrupt controller

interrupt is assigned an INT number from among the available 256 interrupts, such as INT08H for IRQ1 and INT76H for IRQ14.

Programmable interrupt controller (PIC)

To enable the various IRQs to share the single processor INTR line, the PC uses the 8259A programmable interrupt controller (PIC). Being a programmable chip, the 8259A contains a number of registers which are used by BIOS to load the list of IRQs and their individual INT numbers during the boot-up stage.

The 8259A (Fig. 9.4) can handle up to eight different interrupts, numbered IRQ0 to IRQ7 in decreasing order of hierarchical priority. The interrupt controller stores the list of IRQs as they arrive, evaluates their priority (low numbers have higher priority) and issues an interrupt request signal to the CPU. When the processor is ready to deal with the interrupt, it sends back an interrupt acknowledge (INTA) signal. In response, the interrupt controller places the interrupt number on the data bus which enables the processor to identify the appropriate interrupt vector and subsequently the start address of the handler routine.

To extend the number of hardware interrupts, a cascaded master/ slave arrangement employing a pair of 8259A chips is used as shown in Fig. 9.5. The chip which feeds directly to the CPU is known as the master controller. Its interrupt level 2, IRQ2, receives an input from the second PIC known as the slave. A total of 15 interrupts thus become available: IRQ0, IRQ1 and IRQ3 to IRQ15. The cascade connection provides the priority arrangement shown in Table 9.1. Top priority level is still given to IRQ0 followed by IRQ1 and IRQ2. However, because the slave is cascaded to IRQ2, the interrupts provided by the slave controller are assigned the next level of priority.

Table 9.1 also lists the standard INT vector numbers assigned for each interrupt and their functions. It should be noted that five interrupts (IRQ0, IRQ1, IRQ2, IRQ8 and IRQ13) are designated the specific functions listed. These interrupts are not available on an expansion bus. The other interrupts, which are available on

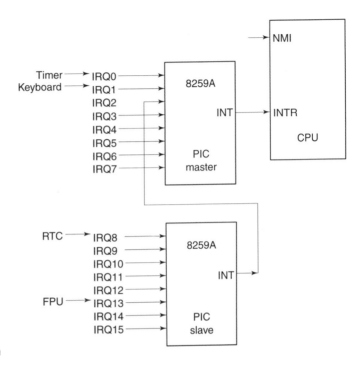

Figure 9.5 Cascaded PIC connection

Table 9.1

Priority level	IRQ no.	Function	Expansion bus	INT no.
Highest	0	System timer	Not available	08H
	1	Keyboard controller	Not available	09H
	2	Cascade IRQ	Not available	A0H
	8	Real-time clock	Not available	70H
	9	User selected	Available (8-bit)	71H
	10	User selected	Available (8-bit)	72H
	11	User selected	Available (16-bit)	73H
	12	On-board mouse port	Available (16-bit)	74H
	13	Maths coprocessor	Not available	75H
	14	Hard disk controller	Available (16-bit)	76H
	15	User selected	Available (16-bit)	77H
	3	Serial COM2/COM4	Available (8-bit)	0BH
	4	Serial COM1/COM3	Available (8-bit)	0CH
	5	Parallel LPT2/LPT4	Available (8-bit)	0DH
	6	Floppy disk controller	Available (8-bit)	0EH
Lowest	7	Parallel LPT1/LPT3	Available (8-bit)	0FH

expansion buses, are usually used for the functions listed. Three interrupts (IRQ9, IRQ10 and IRQ11) are not assigned any specific function. It will also be noticed that IRQ3 and IRQ4 are shared between serial ports COM2/COM4 and COM1/COM3, and IRQ5 and IRQ7 are shared between LPT2/LPT4 and LPT1/LPT3.

10 Input/output adaptors

Input/output adaptors provide serial and parallel data communication between the PC and peripheral devices such as a printer, a mouse or a modem. A PC supports four serial paths (COM1–COM4) and four parallel paths (LPT1–LPT4). Both the serial and parallel portions of the adaptor are fully programmable to meet the different requirements of external devices. Two input/output interface devices are used: a UART (Universal Asynchronous Receiver Transmitter) for serial and a PIA (Peripheral Interface Adaptor) or PPI (Programmable Peripheral Interface) for parallel data transfer.

I/O adaptor cards normally provide a games port as well as floppy and hard disk drive controller circuitry.

ASCII Data communication may take the form of the transfer of pages of text in which case the alphanumeric characters must first be converted into digitally coded packets. The most extensively used code is ASCII (American Standard Code for Information Interchange). In ASCII, each character is represented by a 7-bit code, b0–b6 (Fig. 10.1). The eighth bit (b7) is available for parity checking. With a 7-bit code, a maximum of 2^7 or 128 different characters may be represented. Of these 128 characters, 96 are used for the normal printing characters (including upper and lower cases). The remaining 32 characters are non-printing functions such as carriage return, line feed, backspace and delete. Table 10.1 lists the complete set of ASCII coded characters.

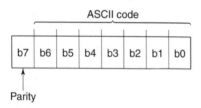

ASCII code

| b7 | b6 | b5 | b4 | b3 | b2 | b1 | b0 |

Parity

Figure 10.1 The 8-bit ASCII code with parity

Interfacing with the processor The purpose of an interface, be it a serial, a parallel or a disk drive interface, is to provide a facility for the movement of data between the computer and an external device. To perform this task, interface adaptors provide one or more 8-bit registers, known as I/O ports, for data storage. Data transfer then takes place by the processor moving data between a memory location and an I/O port. There are two

Table 10.1

Character	Decimal	HEX	Character	Decimal	HEX
NUL	0	00h	!	33	21h
SOH	1	01h	"	34	22h
STX	2	02h	#	35	23h
ETX	3	03h	$	36	24h
EOT	4	04h	%	37	25h
ENQ	5	05h	&	38	26h
ACK	6	06h	'	39	27h
BEL	7	07h	(	40	28h
BS	8	08h	)	41	29h
HT	9	09h	*	42	2Ah
LF	10	0Ah	+	43	2Bh
VT	11	0Bh	,	44	2Ch
FF	12	0Ch	−	45	2Dh
CR	13	0Dh	.	46	2Eh
SO	14	0Eh	/	47	2Fh
SI	15	0Fh	0	48	30h
DLE	16	10h	1	49	31h
DC1	17	11h	2	50	32h
DC2	18	12h	3	51	33h
DC3	19	13h	4	52	34h
DC4	20	14h	5	53	35h
NAK	21	15h	6	54	36h
SYN	22	16h	7	55	37h
ETB	23	17h	8	56	38h
CAN	24	18h	9	57	39h
EM	25	19h	:	58	3Ah
SUB	26	1Ah	;	59	3Bh
ESC	27	1Bh	<	60	3Ch
FS	28	1Ch	=	61	3Dh
GS	29	1Dh	>	62	3Eh
RS	30	1Eh	?	63	3Fh
US	31	1Fh	@	64	40h
SP	32	20h	A	65	41h

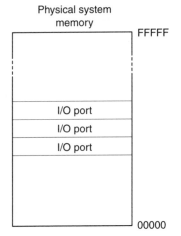

Figure 10.2 Memory mapped I/O ports

different methods of transferring data to and from the I/O port: memory-mapped I/O and isolated I/O. Both methods involve assigning the interface register an address.

In the memory-mapped method, each interface register or I/O port, is assigned an address within the system memory space as shown in Fig. 10.2. The port thus behaves like any other memory location and data may be moved in or out using normal processor instructions. This method has the advantage of programming flexibility but has the disadvantage of occupying parts of the physical memory of the system thus reducing the amount of memory available for application programs. For this reason, memory-mapped I/O is not normally employed.

Table 10.1 (Continued)

Character	Decimal	HEX	Character	Decimal	HEX
B	66	42h	a	97	61h
C	67	43h	b	98	62h
D	68	44h	c	99	63h
E	69	45h	d	100	64h
F	70	46h	e	101	65h
G	71	47h	f	102	66h
H	72	48h	g	103	67h
I	73	49h	h	104	68h
J	74	4Ah	i	105	69h
K	75	4Bh	j	106	6Ah
L	76	4Ch	k	107	6Bh
M	77	4Dh	l	108	6Ch
N	78	4Eh	m	109	6Dh
O	79	4Fh	n	110	6Eh
P	80	50h	o	111	6Fh
Q	81	51h	p	112	70h
R	82	52h	q	113	71h
S	83	53h	r	114	72h
T	84	54h	s	115	73h
U	85	55h	t	116	74h
V	86	56h	u	117	75h
W	87	57h	v	118	76h
X	88	58h	w	119	77h
Y	89	59h	x	120	78h
Z	90	5Ah	y	121	79h
[	91	5Bh	z	122	7Ah
\	92	5Ch	{	123	7Bh
]	93	5Dh	|	124	7Ch
^	94	5Eh	}	125	7Dh
_	95	5Fh	~	126	7Eh
'	96	60h	DEL	127	7Fh

Isolated I/O interfacing

The most common I/O interfacing technique is the isolated memory method. Intel and compatible processors support a separate 64KB I/O memory space, which is entirely distinct from the system's physical memory, where I/O ports can be placed as shown in Fig. 10.3. The I/O memory space consists of 64KB individually addressable 8-bit port locations; 16-bit and 32-bit ports are catered for by using two or four consecutive locations respectively. This memory space is not available as a physical memory bank. It is available in the form of 8-bit registers which are accessed by specified addresses within the I/O memory space.

The I/O memory space is accessed by the CPU using special instructions (IN, OUT, INS and OUTS) together with special control

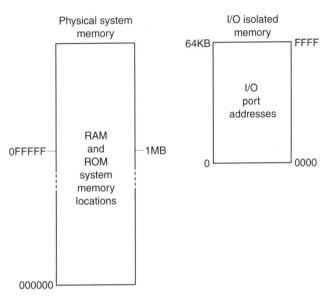

Figure 10.3 Isolated I/O memory

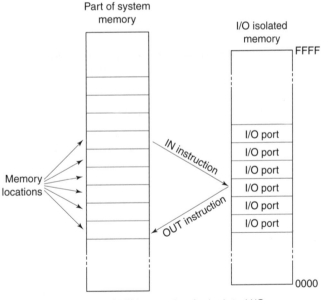

Figure 10.4 IN and OUT instruction for isolated I/O memory

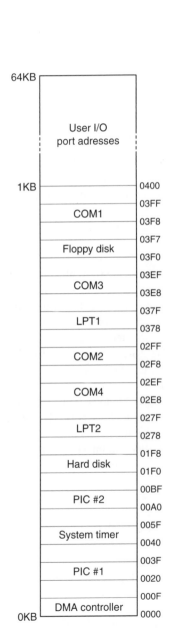

Figure 10.5 I/O memory standard allocations

signals to indicate an I/O addressing rather than normal system memory addressing. An IN instruction moves data from a memory location to an I/O port location, whilst an OUT instruction moves data from a port to a memory location (Fig. 10.4).

This method of data transfer is used for all peripherals such as a disk drive, a mouse or a visual display unit as well as programmable devices such as the interrupt controller, the DMA controller and the system timer. All such devices are allocated port addresses, also known as port numbers, within the isolated I/O memory space.

The first 1KB, a total of 1024 address locations, of the I/O memory space, from 0000H to 03FFH, is reserved for the computer system to allocate to peripherals and devices (Fig. 10.5). Where more than one serial path is provided, e.g COM1 and COM2, separate port numbers or addresses are allocated for each serial communication path: 03F8H to 03FFH for COM1 and 02F8H to 02FFH for COM2.

Serial and parallel port addresses

The serial and parallel I/O interface chips contain more than one register – a total of four in the case of PPI (parallel) and eight in the case of a UART (serial). One register, known as the data register, is used for data transfer. The other registers are used to specify the transfer mode and to process other control requirements. All the registers are given port addresses and are thus directly addressable by the processor with the IN and OUT instructions. The port address of the data register is known as the base address of the device.

RS-232 serial communication

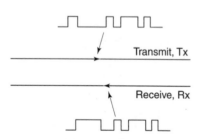

Figure 10.6 Bidirectional serial communications

In serial communication, data bits are sent in the form of a bit stream 1 bit after another along a single connecting wire as shown in Fig. 10.6. A second wire is made available for receiving the serial signal. The most widely used standard for serial communication between PCs, peripheral devices and remote computers is the RS-232 (RS stands for recommended standard). The RS-232 was first defined by the Electronic Industries Association in 1962 and since then a number of variants have been developed.

In the vast majority of systems, asynchronous transmission is employed which does not involve sending a clock pulse. However, start and stop bits are necessary to indicate the beginning and end of a frame or a packet. Asynchronous serial communication consists of a stream of frames or packets, each one containing the data bits and other framing bits (start and stop bits) as well as a parity bit where parity is used. Fig. 10.7 shows the waveform of a serial asynchronous packet using one start bit, two stop bits and odd parity. The seven data bits are the ASCII character code for E (1000101 or 45 in HEX). The beginning of the packet is indicated by a start bit which is always LOW irrespective of the contents of the packet. This is followed by the 7-bit ASCII code for the character E with the least significant bit (LSB) sent first. A parity bit is then added followed by two stop bits which are set HIGH. The complete packet thus comprises 11 bits of which seven are data bits, three are framing bits and one is a parity bit.

The speed by which the bits are sent, i.e the rate of transmission,

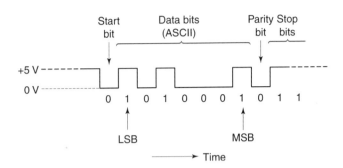

Figure 10.7 Typical asynchronous transmission signal

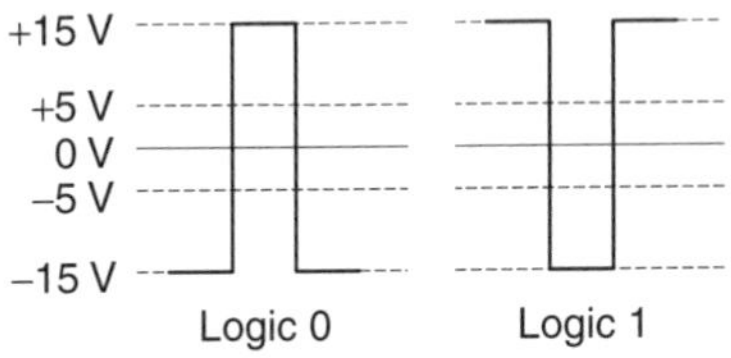

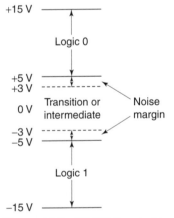

Figure 10.8 RS-232 voltage levels

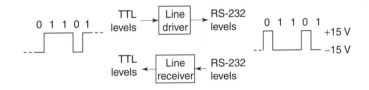

Figure 10.9 RS-232 threshold voltages

is given by the number of signalling elements (in this case bits) per second. This is known as the baud rate. Baud rates of 2400 and 4800 are common.

The RS-232 voltage levels

The voltage levels used within a PC are TTL levels in which a logic 1 is nominally represented by 5 V and a logic 0 is nominally represented by 0 V. Signals of that level cannot be transmitted reliably over a long distance. To increase the working distance of serial cables, high voltage levels are used. RS-232 specifications are as follows: logic 0 is represented by a positive voltage range of between +5 V and +15 V and logic 1 is represented by a negative voltage of between −5 V and −15V as shown in Fig. 10.8. This allows the RS-232 to communicate over a distance of 100 feet (30 metres). A 2 V noise margin is allowed with levels falling between −3 V and +3 V treated as indeterminate, as shown in Fig. 10.9. Level shifting from TTL to RS-232 and vice versa must therefore take place before signals are sent along a serial RS-232 link. This is accomplished by a line driver which shifts TTL levels to RS-232 levels and a line receiver which shifts RS-232 levels to TTL levels (Fig. 10.10).

Figure 10.10 The line driver and the line receiver

Serial interface The serial interface is based around a fully programmable 8-bit 8250 or a 16-bit 16450/16550 UART chip. Although a discrete UART chip may not be used, its function is none the less incorporated and performed by specialised multi-purpose ASICs (Application-Specific Integrated Circuits).

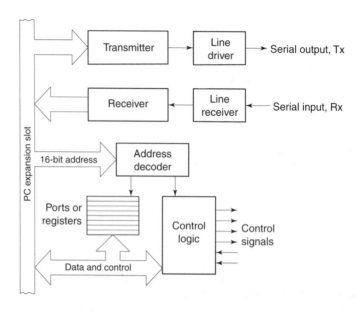

Figure 10.11 UART block diagram

The UART has two modes of operation:

1. The transmit mode, in which the device takes parallel data from the PC and converts it into a serial signal, Tx, with appropriate start, stop and parity bits, and other control signals.
2. The receive mode, in which the chip receives a serial signal, Rx, from a peripheral device and converts it into a parallel format.

A simplified block diagram of a UART is shown in Fig. 10.11. The transmitter contains all the necessary circuitry for parallel to serial conversion. Conversely, the receiver contains the necessary circuitry for serial to parallel conversion. The integrated line driver and receiver provide voltage shifting from TTL levels to RS-232 levels and vice versa respectively. The address decoder receives the 16-bit address and directs the processor to the appropriate register or port. The control logic unit specifies the mode of operation, its baud rate and its format (word length, stop bits and parity). It also monitors the progress of the operation informing the processor of any problems and processes the control signals to and from the peripheral devices.

Eight different registers are provided by the UART: the data register which is known as the base register and seven other registers used to regulate the operation and monitor its progress (Fig. 10.12). The data register acts as a receive buffer when the UART is in the receive mode or a transmit buffer when the UART is in the transmit mode. The contents of other registers set the baud rate, enable or disable the parity bit, set the number of stop bits, inform the processor on the status of the operation and set modem parameters. All eight registers are allocated port numbers or addresses and as such are fully addressable by the processor and may be accessed by an IN or an OUT instruction. The

UART registers	Port addresses
User	Base + 07
UART status	Base + 06
Line status	Base + 05
Modem control	Base + 04
Data frame	Base + 03
Interrupt ID	Base + 02
Baud rate	Base + 01
Data	Base address

Figure 10.12 UART registers

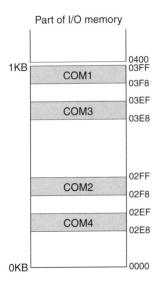

Part of I/O memory

Figure 10.13 Serial ports base addresses

User	03FF
UART status	03FE
Line status	03FD
Modem control	03FC
Data frame	03FB
Interrupt ID	03FA
Baud rate	03F9
Data	03F8 (base)

Figure 10.14 COM1 base and other register addresses

data register is normally allocated the lowest port number, known as the base address, with the other registers allocated consecutive addresses. The four communication ports, COM1 to COM4, are allocated the following blocks of port addresses:

COM1   03F8H (base address) to 03FFH
COM2   02F8H (base address) to 02FFH
COM3   03E8H (base address) to 03EFH
COM4   02E8H (base address) to 02EFH

Fig. 10.13 shows the allocations for all four serial ports and Fig. 10.14 shows the port addresses of COM1.

The block of port addresses for each serial port is identified by their base address, e.g. COM1 by port address 03F8H, COM2 by 02F8H and so on. During boot-up, BIOS searches for COM port addresses in the order listed above and loads the base addresses of installed serial ports at the start of the system memory space allocated for BIOS data commencing at address 0400H. DOS then assigns COM1 to the first base address that it finds, COM2 to the second and so on to COM4. The base addresses are listed in two consecutive 1-byte locations with the low byte occupying the lower location. Fig. 10.15 shows the contents of the BIOS data space of a PC with two serial ports, COM1 and COM2. If a third serial port is installed, COM3, its base address 03E8H would be stored in locations 0404H and 0405H.

Address	0400	0401	0402	0403	0404	0405	0406	0407
data	F8	03	F8	02	00	00	00	00

COM1   COM2   COM3 not installed   COM4 not installed

Figure 10.15 Contents of BIOS data space for a PC with two comports

COM port addressing   Before a serial port outlet is used for data transfer, the processor must first initialise the selected COM port. Initialisation of a serial

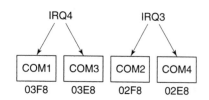

Figure 10.16 COM port base address and IRQ allocation

port involves loading the registers with the appropriate control bits to set the mode, format, baud rate and parity. Before initialisation can take place, the processor must ascertain the addresses of the ports associated with the COM port that has been selected. This is achieved by fetching the COM port base address from the appropriate locations in the BIOS data memory space. For instance, if serial port COM1 is to be addressed by the PC, the processor will fetch its base address at locations 0400H and 0401H from which the serial port address block is identified. Having identified the port addresses, the processor proceeds to load them with the appropriate control bits to initialise the device.

The process starts with the serial interface invoking a hardware interrupt, IRQ. The programmable interrupt controls, PIC chip receiving the IRQ informs the processor of the INT number

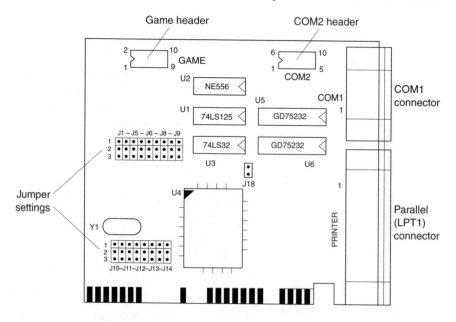

Jumper settings for COM1 and COM2:

Port address

J6	J7	COM 2		J8	J9	COM 1
1-2	1-2	2F8h		1-2	1-2	2F8h
1-2	2-3	2E8h		1-2	2-3	3E8h
2-3	1-2	3F8h		2-3	1-2	2F8h
2-3	2-3	Disable		2-3	2-3	Disable

IRQ setting

	COM2	COM1	
J10	1-2 : IRQ3	2-3 : IRQ3	Game port setting
J11	1-2 : IRQ4	2-3 : IRQ4	
J12	1-2 : IRQ5	2-3 : IRQ5	J18 : Game select
J13	1-2 : IRQ7	2-3 : IRQ7	ON : Game Enable
J14	1-2 : IRQ9	2-3 : IRQ9	OFF : Game Disable

Figure 10.17 Typical I/O expansion card

associated with the IRQ. The processor examines the interrupt vector table to identify the interrupt vector and hence the start address of the interrupt handler routine. The processor then initialises the UART before it calls and runs the handler routine for data to be transferred.

Two IRQs are designated for the use of serial ports: IRQ3 for COM2 and IRQ4 for COM1. Where more than two serial ports are installed, the interrupt requests are shared as follows:

IRQ3 shared between COM2 and COM4
IRQ4 shared between COM1 and COM3

Sharing IRQs between peripheral devices causes what is known as interrupt conflict and hence it is not normally permitted. However, a single IRQ may be shared between two hardware devices, such as two serial ports, provided they are not used at the same time. While two serial ports may share a single IRQ in this way, the same cannot be said of port addresses. Each COM port must have its own individual base address (Fig. 10.16).

Both port addresses and IRQs must be assigned to each available serial port before booting up the PC. This may be carried out by jumper settings on the adaptor card or through CMOS set-up configuration. A typical jumper setting is shown in Fig. 10.17.

Parallel interface

In parallel communication, data and control bits are transmitted simultaneously along a number of parallel lines, one line for each bit of data as shown in Fig. 10.18. Compared with the serial mode, parallel communication is fast and more straightforward in that it does not require serial/parallel conversion. Originally, the PC parallel connection was intended for the use of printers – hence their name LPT (line printer) or PRN (printer) ports. The PC supports three parallel paths known as LPT1, LPT2 and LPT3.

Parallel cables are normally restricted to not more than 10 feet (3 metres) in length. Longer cables may cause unacceptable levels of crosstalk between one signal on one line and another signal on an adjacent parallel line.

Three registers known as ports are provided by the parallel interface: a data register for data transfer, a control register for generating and interpreting control signals and a status register to monitor the status of data transfer. Parallel I/O registers are addressed in the same way as serial ports. Each register is allocated an I/O port number or address within the I/O isolated memory space with access to the ports obtained by an IN or an OUT instruction. The data register is allocated the base address which is then referred to as the parallel port address as shown in Fig. 10.19. The three parallel ports are allocated the following port addresses:

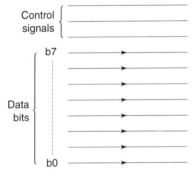

Figure 10.18 Parallel transmission

I/O register or ports

Status	Base + 02
Control	Base + 01
Data	Base address

Figure 10.19 Parallel port registers

LPT1   03BCH
LPT2   0378H
LPT3   0278H

Most compatible systems avoid using port address 03BCH. Instead, 0378H is allocated for LPT1 and 0278H is allocated for LPT2. It is unusual for three parallel ports to be installed.

During boot-up, BIOS searches for parallel port addresses in the order listed above (i.e. 03BC, 0378, 0278) and loads them into the BIOS data memory space commencing at address 0408H, immediately following the serial port addresses. DOS then assigns LPT1 to the first base address that it finds, LPT2 to the second and so on. The base addresses are listed in two consecutive 1-byte locations with the low byte occupying the lower location. Fig. 10.20 shows the typical contents of the BIOS data space of a PC with two serial ports, COM1 and COM2, and two parallel ports, LPT1 and LPT2.

Two IRQs are designated for the use of parallel ports: IRQ7 to be shared between LPT1 and LPT3, and IRQ5 for LPT2. Where LPT4 is installed, it has to share IRQ5 with LPT2.

Address	0400	0401	0402	0403	0404	0405	0406	0407	0408	0409	040A	040B	040C	040D
data	F8	03	F8	02	00	00	00	00	78	03	78	02	00	00
	COM1		COM2		Not installed		Not installed		LPT1		LPT2		Not installed	

Figure 10.20   Contents of BIOS data space for a PC with two comports and two parallel ports

11 Serial and parallel ports

The main methods of communication between a computer and a peripheral are via the serial or parallel connectors available at the back of the system unit of the PC. These connectors are known as ports, not to be confused with addressable I/O ports. The serial mode is used primarily for bidirectional communications between a PC and a peripheral device such as mouse, a modem or a scanner. The parallel port is primarily used for unidirectional communication with a peripheral such as a printer. However, bidirectional parallel ports are also available.

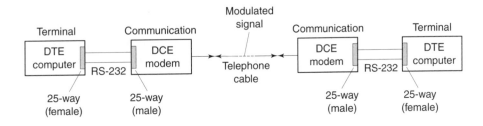

Figure 11.1 Communication using a telephone line

The RS-232 serial cable   The RS-232 standard was designed for long distance communication using a telephone line as shown in Fig. 11.1. A modem (modulator/ demodulator) known as data communication equipment (DCE) is used at each end to convert the digital signal from the serial port into a modulated signal suitable to be sent along a telephone line. Two modems are needed, one at each end of the telephone line. The computer itself is referred to as data terminal equipment (DTE). The RS-232 specification provides two data lines, transmit data (TD) and receive data (RD), together with six control lines to carry what are known as handshaking signals to ensure that the exchange of data only occurs when both the DTE (computer) and the DCE (modem) are correctly set and ready to process the data.

Serial port signals   Fig. 11.2 shows the data and handshake lines between a DTE (computer) and a DCE (modem). One line is allocated for transmit data, TD (pin 2), and a second line is allocated for receive data, RD (pin 3). Two other lines are used for ground (pin 7) and protected ground (pin 1). The other six lines are used for handshake and control signals.

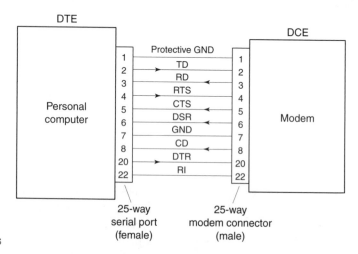

Figure 11.2 Data and handshake lines

Before data begins to flow three requirements are necessary: first a connection must be established between the computer terminal (DTE) and the modem (DCE). Secondly, a telephone carrier signal (i.e. a dialing tone) must be detected by the modem. Thirdly, having established a connection, data exchange will take place when the computer indicates its readiness to send data and the modem indicates its readiness to receive data.

Making a connection, DTR/DSR

When the computer is initialised by the appropriate I/O routine, it indicates its readiness for data exchange by invoking the data terminal ready (DTR) signal. Similarly, following its own initialisation by the appropriate software routine, the modem invokes the data set ready (DSR) signal indicating its readiness to receive data. A connection is thus established between the DTE (computer) and the DCE (modem). This DTR/DSR handshake must be maintained throughout the data exchange. If it is broken, transmission will cease.

Carrier detect (CD)

Where the connection is via a telephone line, data transfer takes place only when the modem establishes that a carrier signal is present on the telephone line, in which case it sends a carrier detect (CD) signal to the computer.

Data flow control, CTS/RTS

Data transfer takes place when the computer generates a clear to send (CTS) signal and the modem invokes the ready to receive (RTS) signal. Data begins to flow and continues to do so until the buffers at the receiving end become full. When this happens, the RTS signal is disabled and data flow is halted. It recommences when the buffers are emptied and the RTS line is reasserted. This handshake forms the basis of what is known as CTS/RTS data flow control.

The ring indicator (RI)

The ring indicator is used when the attention of the computer is requested. It is asserted by the modem when a telephone ring is detected from a remote terminal.

The serial port connector

Access to the serial port is provided by a 25-way D-type (male) connector (Fig. 11.3). The pin-out functions are listed in Table 11.1.

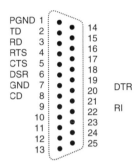

Figure 11.3   Pin-out of 25-way D-type male serial connector

Table 11.1

Pin no.	Function	
1	Protective ground	PGND
2	Transmit data	TD or TX
3	Receive data	RD or RX
4	Request to send	RTS
5	Clear to send	CTS
6	Data set ready	DSR
7	Ground	GND
8	Carrier detect	CD or DCD
20	Data terminal ready	DTR
22	Ring indicator	RI

The null-modem serial link

Although the RS-232 was designed to be used with a modem, it is invariably used for direct communication between one DTE such as a computer and another DTE such as a second computer or a printer. Serial DTE-to-DTE communication may be carried out in several ways, all of which require a specially assembled RS-232 cable known as a null-modem or DTE-to-DTE cable.

The normal serial cable used to connect a DTE to a DCE is a straight cable which connects the pins on the computer's serial port to the corresponding pins on the modem: pin 2 to pin 2, pin 3 to pin 3 and so on as shown in Fig. 11.4. Data from A is sent from pin 2 on computer terminal A to pin 2 on modem A. Modem A transmits the

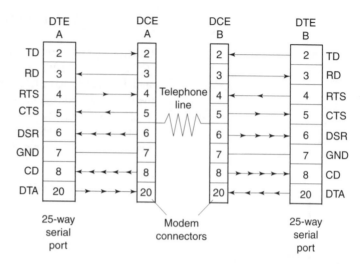

Figure 11.4

data along a telephone line to modem B which sends the data to terminal computer B along the RD line, pin 3 to pin 3. Thus data appearing on pin 2 (TD) on computer A ends up at pin 3 (RD) on computer B. Conversely, when data is sent from B to A, it appears on pin 2 on terminal computer B and ends at pin 3 on terminal computer A. Furthermore, before data is sent, the RTS/CTS data flow control must be established: the RTS signal on pin 4 on terminal A and the CTS signal on modem A are invoked. At the other end the RTS signal on pin 4 on terminal B and the CTS signal on modem B are invoked. Similarly for the DTR/DSR handshake combination. The carrier detect signals (not shown) are generated by the modems themselves and are fed into the respective control pins of the computer terminal connections.

Once the modems are removed, the two computer serial connectors face each other with no intermediary. Since each computer transmits and receives data on the same pin numbers, i.e. pins 2 (TD) and pins 3 (RD) respectively, then in order for data transmitted from one end (pin 2) to arrive at the other end (pin 3) the two lines must be crossed over as shown in Fig. 11.5. Together with the ground connections, this forms the basic two-way communication between two DTEs. In practice, some form of handshaking is involved to ensure that both devices can keep up with the flow of data. Such data flow control may take the form of hardware (RTS/CTS or DTR/DSR) or software (X-ON/X-OFF).

Hardware flow control can take the form of RTS/CTS or DTR/DSR or both. RTS/CTS control is accomplished by connecting pin 4 (RTS) to pin 5 (CTS) and DRT/DSR is accomplished by connecting pin 20 (DTR) to pin 6 (DSR) as illustrated in Fig. 11.6. The same effect may be produced if pin 4 (RTS) is connected to pin 6 (DSR) and pin 20 (DTR) is connected to pin 5 (CTS). Although carrier detect (CD) is no longer relevant in DTE-to-DTE connection and

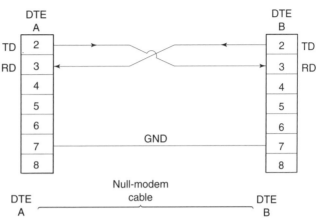

Figure 11.5

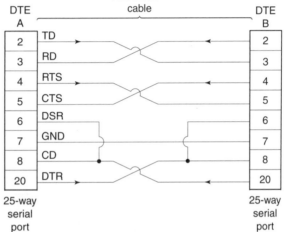

Figure 11.6 The null-modem (DTE-to-DTE) serial cable

may be left unconnected, pin 8 is normally enabled by connecting pin 20 (DTR) of one end to pin 8 (CD) of the other. The CD pin will thus be enabled whenever the other terminal indicates that it is ready for data exchange. Such a cable is known as a cross-over cable, DTE-to-DTE cable or a null-modem cable.

X-ON/X-OFF

X-ON/X-OFF uses standard ASCII control characters to control the flow of data between two intelligent terminals such as two computers or a computer and a printer. In most systems, Ctrl-S sends X-OFF to stop further data transmission and Ctrl-Q sends X-ON to resume transmission. A simple two-wire serial cable may be used with the control/handshake lines enabled as shown in Fig. 11.7.

The 9-way serial port connector

PCs normally provide a second, smaller 9-way D-type (male) serial port in addition to the 25-way port. In this version (Fig. 11.8), pins 2

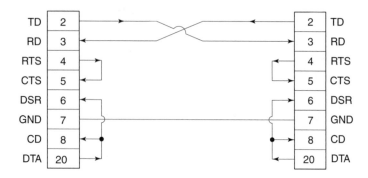

Figure 11.7 2-wire serial DTE-to-DTE communication

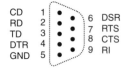

Figure 11.8 Pin-out of a 9-way serial connector (male)

and 3 are used for receive and transmit respectively. Table 11.2 lists the pin-out functions of a 9-way serial port connector. With both 25-way and 9-way serial ports in common use, null-modem cables with different types of connectors at either end may be required. Table 11.3 lists the complete cross-over connections for null-modem cables with all three possible combinations.

Table 11.2

Pin no.	Function	
1	Carrier detect	CD
2	Receive data	RD or RX
3	Transmit data	TD or TX
4	Data terminal ready	DTR
5	Ground	GND
6	Data set ready	DSR
7	Request to send	RTS
8	Clear to send	CTS
9	Ring indicator	RI

Table 11.3

Signal	25–25 pins s/c	25–9 pins s/c	9–9 pins s/c
TX–RX	2–3	2–2	2–3
RX–TX	3–2	3–3	3–2
DTR–DSR	20–6	20–6	4–6
DSR–DTR	6–20	6–4	6–4
RTS–CTS	4–5	4–8	7–8
CTS–RTS	5–4	5–7	8–7
CD–DTR	8–20	8–4	1–4
DTR–CD	20–8	20–1	4–1
GND	7–7	7–5	5–5

Testing the serial port – the loopback test

The serial port and adaptor may be tested by a software routine available with most diagnostic utilities such as PC Doctor, or Microscope. The test routine tests data transmission and reception at different baud rates as well as testing the data and other UART registers. To enable the test to take place, a special loopback block (Fig. 11.9) is connected to the port under test to simulate a serial link to another computer or a modem. Data transmit (pin 2) is looped back to data receive (pin 3), RTS (pin 4) is looped back to CTS (pin 5) and DTR (pin 20) is looped back to DSR and CD (pins 6 and 8).

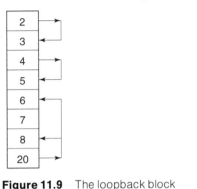

Figure 11.9   The loopback block

The breakout box (BoB)

The RS-232 breakout box (BoB) was originally designed to allow the user to cross over two or more serial lines to produce the right set of connections for the particular application. The BoB also provides a facility to monitor the logic activity of each line.

The BoB (Fig. 11.10) consists of two connectors, a DTE and a DCE, which connect to the computer and a peripheral device such as a modem or a printer. A set of switches are provided which may be used to break a line and, by using jumper leads, a cross-over of lines can take place as required. The BoB also provides a set of LEDs to indicate the logic state of each line: logic HIGH, logic LOW or pulse.

The BoB may also be used to test a suspected faulty cable. The BoB is first connected to one side of the cable and then to the other. Each time, the logic states of the lines are noted with the handshake and control lines turned off and on. The state of TD and RD are also observed as a data exchange is attempted. An open circuit line, a short circuit between lines or wrong pin connections may thus be diagnosed. Faults such as a wrong pin connection may be rectified using appropriate break switches and cross-over jumper wires.

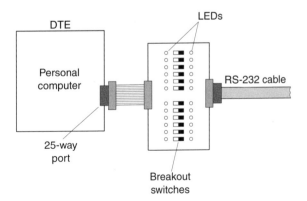

Figure 11.10   The breakout box (BoB)

Parallel port connection

The original computer parallel port, known as the standard parallel port (SPP), was designed for 8-bit unidirectional communication with a printer. MS-DOS provides the necessary software routines for ASCII-coded alphanumeric characters to be transferred from the PC to the printer.

The 25-way parallel port

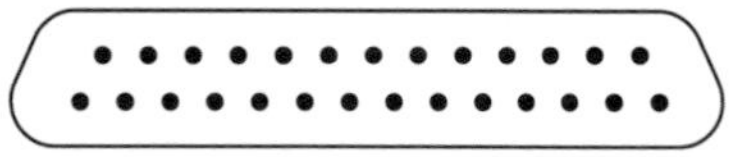

On the computer side, access to the parallel port is available as a 25-way D-shell female-type connector (Fig. 11.11). On the printer side a 35-way Centronics connector is used (Fig. 11.12).

The standard parallel port sends packets of 8-bit data along eight parallel lines (pins 2–9). Seven other lines are used for handshaking and control functions to ensure that data transfer takes place when both sides are ready (Table 11.4).

Following a print instruction, the computer places the first byte of data on the data lines (pins 2–9), and invokes the strobe signal on pin 1 (logic LOW) indicating that data is valid. If the printer is ready to receive the data, it disables the busy signal on pin 11 (logic LOW) and data is then transferred. The printer then acknowledges receipt of the first byte of data by enabling the acknowledge signal on pin 10 (logic LOW). This process is repeated for the next byte and so on until the printer buffers are full, in which case the busy line goes HIGH and data transfer is halted. The busy line will also be enabled (logic HIGH) if the printer is not initialised or not functioning for

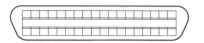

Figure 11.11 25-way D-type (female) parallel connector

Figure 11.12 The 35-way centronics connector

Table 11.4

25-way pin no.	Function	Direction in/out
1	Strobe, STR	Out
2	Data bit 0	Out
3	Data bit 1	Out
4	Data bit 2	Out
5	Data bit 3	Out
6	Data bit 4	Out
7	Data bit 5	Out
8	Data bit 6	Out
9	Data bit 7	Out
10	Acknowledge, ACK	In
11	Busy, BSY	In
12	Paper out, PAPER	In
13	Select, SEL	In
14	Auto feed, AF	Out
15	ERROR	In
16	Initialise printer, INI	Out
17	Device select, DSL	Out
18–25	GROUND	

any reason, such as a stuck ribbon, thus preventing any data transfer from taking place. The process is very fast with the computer able to dump as many as 500,000 bytes of data per second. In practice, such high speeds are not realised. The actual speed of transfer between a computer and a printer depends on the type of printer and the size of its buffers.

The parallel port does more than just move data from computer to printer. It provides other lines which inform the computer of the working condition of the printer: select (pin 13) informs the computer that the printer is on-line; paper out (pin 12) indicates no paper and ERROR indicates other faults causing the printer to stop functioning. Three other signals are used to control various aspects of the printer: auto feed (pin 14) ensures that the paper is advanced one line upon return; device select (pin 17) allows the computer to bring the printer on- and off-line, a facility that is available on some printers; and initialise printer (pin 16) ensures that the printer is set to receive data.

Parallel I/O ports

Base + 2	Control
Base + 1	Status
Base addr.	Data

Figure 11.13 Parallel port registers

Three registers (Fig. 11.13), each with its own individual I/O port address, are allocated for the operation and control of each parallel port: a data register which holds and transfers the 8-bit data, a control register which holds output signals STR, AF, INI and DSL, and a status register which holds input signals ACK, BSY, PAPER, SEL and ERROR. In the case of the unidirectional standard parallel port (SPP), in which the data flow is in one direction, i.e. out of the computer and into the printer, the data register is configured as a WRITE only register. The status register which holds input signals only is configured to be a READ only register and finally the control register which holds output signals is configured as a WRITE only register. The designation of these registers as READ or WRITE is carried out by the BIOS routine setting the appropriate bit in the control register to logic 0 or logic 1.

Bi-directional parallel ports

The standard parallel port (SPP) provides fast 8-bit unidirectional data transfer mainly for the use of a printer. To take advantage of the high speed of data transfer provided by a parallel port for communication between one PC and another, bidirectional parallel ports are required. Over the years, several software routines have been developed to support bidirectional communication using a parallel port, such MS-DOS Interlink, enhanced parallel port (EPP) and the extended capabilities port (ECP).

Interlink nibble data transfer

The MS-DOS interlink routine provides a 4-bit parallel communication link with which two computers communicate with each other

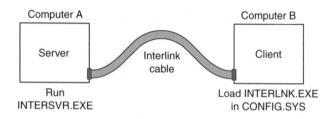

Figure 11.14 INTERLNK computer-to-computer data transfer

This Computer (client)		Other Computer (server)
D:	equals	A:
E:	equals	C:

Figure 11.15 Typical drive allocation using INTERLNK

(Fig. 11.14). One computer is referred to as the server and the other as the client. To run this program, INTERLNK.EXE (note missing 'I') must first be loaded as the device driver in CONFIG.SYS (after other drivers) in the client computer and INTERSVR.EXE is executed in the server computer. The interlink program will allow the server to have access to the drives on the client computer as extra drives using letters above those already used by the server, e.g. D: for client's drive A: and E for client's drive C:, displayed on the screen, as shown in Fig. 11.15.

The DOS interlink routine allows both serial and parallel data transfer. For serial communication, a null-modem or a simple two-wire cable may be used.

Where parallel communication is employed, a special interlink parallel cable known as the interlink or nibble transfer cable must be used. The MS-DOS interlink program does not change the IN/OUT designation of the pins of the parallel port. For this reason data pins of one computer designated as output must be connected to pins that are designated as inputs of the second computer and vice versa. Table 11.5 lists the cross-over connections for an interlink cable.

Table 11.5

25-Pin connector A	25-Pin connector B
1 not connected	1 not connected
2 D0	15 ERROR
3 D1	13 SELECT
4 D2	12 PAPER
5 D3	10 ACK
6 D4	11 BUSY
7 not connected	7 not connected
8 not connected	8 not connected
9 not connected	9 not connected
10 ACK	5 D3
11 BUSY	6 D4
12 PAPER	4 D2
13 SELECT	3 D1
14 not connected	14 not connected
15 ERROR	2 D0
16 not connected	16 not connected
17 not connected	17 not connected
25 GND	25 GND

When computer A is sending data to B, D0–D3 are sent to pins 15 (ERROR), 13 (SELECT), 12 (PAPER) and 10 (ACK), respectively, where they are loaded into the status register acting as a latched input data register for the receiving computer B. This computer uses the first 5 bits of its data register, D0–D4, to provide the necessary five handshake and control signals ERROR, SELECT, PAPER, ACK and BUSY respectively. These signals are fed to pins 15, 13, 12, 10 and 11 respectively as shown in the table. When data is transferred in the opposite direction, from B to A, the arrangements are reversed: data from B, D0–D3, is sent to A's status register acting as a latched input data register and handshaking and control signals are sent from A's data bits D0–D4 to the status register of B. The remaining control signals (STROBE, AUTO FEED, INI and DEVICE SELECT) are not relevant in this form of communication. The relevant pins are therefore left unconnected. The change in the functions of the registers is carried out by the Interlink program.

Enhanced parallel port (EPP)

The enhanced parallel port provides 8-bit as well as 16-bit and 32-bit bidirectional parallel data transfer. It alters the contents of the registers to establish a different function for the various lines. It uses five more extra registers over and above the three available for the standard parallel port which are used to provide facilities such as additional buffers.

Extended capabilities port (ECP)

The extended capabilities port (ECP) establishes a standard protocol for delivering the functions of the enhanced parallel port. In its default mode, the ECP is set to function as a standard parallel port. It has the ability to interrogate the external device and negotiate the fastest possible mode of data transfer. The ECP allows several devices to be connected to the same port, with each one capable of being addressed separately.

Setting the serial port parameter

During boot-up, BIOS sets the parameters of each serial port to its default value. These parameters may be changed by using the MS-DOS command MODE. The form of the command is

MODE COMn BAUD=b PARITY=p DATA=d STOP=s RETRY=t

where n   is the number of serial port, e.g. 1, 2, 3, 4,

   b   specifies the baud rate, e.g. 1200, 2400 or 4800,

   p   specifies the type of parity (E for EVEN, O for ODD and N for NO PARITY),

   d   specifies the number of bits in each package,

   s   specifies the number of stop bits, e.g. 1 or 2, and

t   specifies the action of the computer in case the device is busy (N for no retry if device is busy, P for continue trying, E for report if retry is not successful and R for reporting 'ready' if retry is not successful; the default value is N).

For example, to set serial port 2 to a baud rate of 1200, even parity, eight data bits and one stop bit, the following command line should be used:

MODE COM2 BAUD=1200 PARITY=N DATA=8 STOP=1

The baud rate must be specified. Other parameters, if not specified, remain unchanged.

Redirecting LPT1 to serial port   When a print command is used, DOS sends the output to one of the installed parallel ports, usually LPT1 which is the default port. If the printer is connected to a serial port, the output must be redirected from LPT1 to the appropriate serial port. This is carried out by the MODE command

MODE LPT1=COMn

where n is the number of the serial port. For example, to redirect the output to COM1, the following command line should be used:

MODE LPT1=COM1

The computer will then respond with a message acknowledging the redirection. To cancel the redirection and return back to LPT1, the following command line should be used:

MODE LPT1

The MODE command can be used to check the status of the system devices. MODE by itself will display the status of all devices including the serial and parallel ports. The form of the command is

MODE DEVICE/STA

where STA is status, e.g.

MODE COM1/STA for status of serial port COM1, or
MODE LPT1/STA   for status of parallel port LPT1

12 Direct memory access

Direct memory access (DMA) is the process of transferring data between memory locations and a peripheral device at a high speed without the direct intervention of the processor. DMA transfers are used in applications where large quantities of data are involved, such as refreshing DRAM devices, video displays where the contents of the screen have to be updated at frequent intervals and data exchange between a disk drive and memory. DMA is also used for high speed memory-to-memory transfer of blocks of data.

Processing DMA

A request for DMA is initiated when the HOLD control signal going into the processor is asserted (taken to logic HIGH) by an external device (Fig. 12.1). The processor responds by suspending the execution of its current program and places its address, data and control buses at tristate (i.e. high impedance or open circuit). This causes the processor to appear as if it has been removed from its socket allowing other devices or processors to gain access to the system bus structure. To confirm this, the processor asserts the hold acknowledge (HLDA) signal. Data transfer then takes place at a speed constrained only by the limitations of the memory chips and the external device making the request. At the end of the transfer, control is handed back to the processor when the external device drops the HOLD signal by taking it back to logic LOW. The processor then returns to the original program.

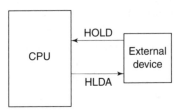

Figure 12.1 DMA control signals

The DMA controller (DMAC)

The processor has a single HOLD control pin which must be shared between all the devices that wish to use DMA. To enable this to happen, the 8237A DMA controller (DMAC) is used (Fig. 12.2). Although the 8237A may not appear as a discrete chip on the motherboard, its function is none the less included within system controller chips or other ASIC packages.

The 8237A is a special purpose programmable microprocessor designed for high speed data transfer. It is capable of DMA transfers at rates up to 1.6MB per second. A single 8237A DMAC chip can handle up to four separate DMA channels with each channel capable of addressing a full 64KB section of memory, including I/O isolated memory space.

Data transfer operation

DMA transfer is initiated with a DMA request (DREQ, or DRQ) signal generated by the device requesting the transfer (Fig. 12.2). When the DMAC receives the DMA request signal, it sends a HOLD request to the processor which suspends its program, and answers with an HLDA signal back to the DMAC. The controller then instructs the bus controller effectively to disconnect the processor from the bus lines. The bus is now under the control of the DMAC which sends a DMA acknowledge (DACK) signal back to the device requesting the DMA indicating that data transfer may begin. Before the transfer can commence, the block of data to be transferred is indicated by its start address (loaded into the base address register of the DMAC) and the number of bytes to be transferred (loaded into the word count register). The DMAC then issues the necessary command signals to accomplish a memory-to-I/O or I/O-to-memory or memory-to-memory transfer. A block of 64KB of data known as a page may be transferred by this process. The process may be repeated for transfers greater than 64KB.

To extend the number of DMA channels, two 8237A devices are used in cascade as shown in Fig. 12.3. A total of seven DMA channels thus become available: four DMA channels (0–3) from the first or master DMA controller and three DMA channels (5–7) from the second or slave DMA controller. DMA channel 4 (DMAC #1) is used as the cascaded input from the second controller and thus is not available. As can be seen from Table 12.1, which lists the DMA channels of an AT computer, DMA channel 2 is allocated for the use of a floppy disk drive. The other channels are available for the user to allocate as necessary. As with interrupts, DMA conflict must be avoided. A DMA channel is selected by software or by setting one or more physical jumpers or DIP switches available on the expansion board.

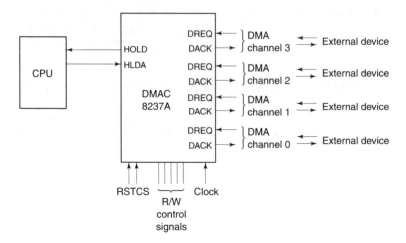

Figure 12.2 DMA controller data and control pins

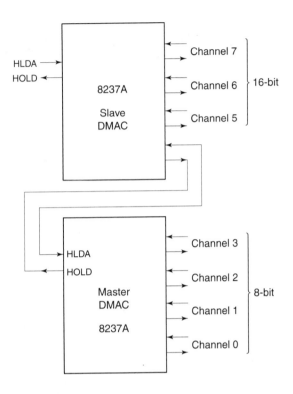

Figure 12.3 Cascaded master/slave
DMAC organisation

Table 12.1

DMA	Function	Bit width
0	User	8-bit
1	User	8-bit
2	Floppy disk controller	8-bit
3	User	8-bit
4	DMAC #1 cascade input*	16-bit
5	User	16-bit
6	User	16-bit
7	User	16-bit

* Not available on expansion bus.

DMA registers
Four fully addressable registers are available for each DMA channel: the base address register which contains the base or start address of the memory block being addressed, the current word count register which contains the number of words to be transferred, and two other registers (the current address and the current word count) which keep track of the transfer of data, byte by byte. The registers for the master DMAC are allocated I/O port addresses 0000H to 000FH and those for the slave controller are allocated port address 00C0H to 00DFH. The latter uses even port addresses only – hence the 32 I/O ports.

13 Disks and disk drives

Disk drives are the primary storage facility in a PC. Two types are normally incorporated in a computer system: the floppy (or removable) disk and the hard (or fixed) disk drives. The basic principles of operation are the same for both types although the hard disk drive has a much larger capacity. Floppy disks have capacities ranging from a few hundred kilobytes to a couple of megabytes while a modern hard disk can store up to a few gigabytes of data.

Magnetic data recording

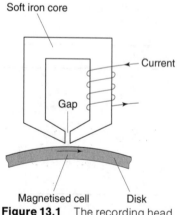

Figure 13.1 The recording head

Data recording on a disk is carried out in the same way as audio signals are recorded onto a magnetic tape. A flat disk of either plastic (the floppy disk) or metal (the hard disk) is coated with a thin layer of magnetic material. The disk is made to rotate under a recording (or writing) head containing a small gap across which a magnetic flux is created by passing a current through a coil (Fig. 13.1). The flux is used to magnetise a small area of the magnetic surface known as a cell to store a logic 0 data bit. If the current is reversed, the cell will be magnetised in the opposite direction to store a logic 1. As the disk rotates under the head, a sequence of magnetised cells is created along a circular track (Fig. 13.2). A second recording track may be used by shifting the head across the surface of the disk.

Data bits stored on the disk may be retrieved by reversing the process using a reading head which detects the magnetic field created by the magnetised cell moving across the gap. The flux induces a voltage across the coil and as successive cells move across the head, a sequence of pulses representing the sequence of bits stored in the cells is produced. By shifting the head across the surface of the disk, data may be retrieved track by track. Two separate heads, one for reading and a second for writing, may be used. However, a single read/write head is adequate and more economical.

Recording data on a disk, a process known as writing, involves producing a magnetic flux across the writing gap at the instant when the particular cell is present. A second magnetising pulse must be produced for the second cell and so on. The cells are thus written at a

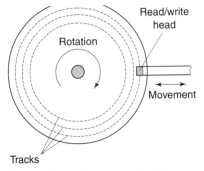

Figure 13.2   The magnetic disk

specific rate determined by the speed of disk rotation and the closeness of the cells. Retrieving the contents of each cell, a process known as reading the disk, involves capturing the magnetic field of each cell as it moves across the head at the angular speed of the disk. The rate at which the cells are read, the sampling rate, must be the same as that used to record them. A change in the sampling rate caused by a slight change in the speed of rotation, for instance, will distort the information by either reading the same cell more than once or missing a cell altogether. To avoid this, self-clocking is used in which the flux reversal induced by the two adjacent cells with opposite magnetisation is used to synchronise the sampling clock. Provided such reversals of flux occur at regular intervals, i.e. at least once in any sequence of three cells, the sampling clock can be kept in sync and the data will always be read correctly. To ensure the required frequency of flux reversal, special coding techniques are used for data recording on disks.

Disk coding techniques

The simplest method of recording data on a magnetic disk is frequency modulation (FM). In this method, flux reversal is introduced at the beginning of each bit. Logic 1 is identified by an additional flux reversal half way through the bit as shown in Fig. 13.3. In other words, a logic 1 is recorded at twice the frequency of that used for logic 0. Recording density, i.e. the number of bits recorded per inch of track provided by this technique, is low since two cells must be made available to record each bit of data. For this reason, FM recording is not used. Instead, more efficient techniques are employed: the modified frequency modulation (MFM) technique is used in floppy disk drives and the run-length-limited (RLL) technique is used in hard disk drives.

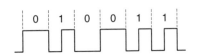

Figure 13.3   Simple frequency modulation (FM) pulse sequence

In MFM, flux reversal is introduced at the start of each bit provided the current and previous bits are zeros. Otherwise, the flux reversal occurs midway through the logic 1 bit as is the case for the simple FM coding method. As can be seen from Fig. 13.4, using MFM coding, only one flux reversal is needed for each bit which doubles the recording density compared with the simple FM coding technique.

The RLL technique specifies a maximum and a minimum number of bits known as a run between flux reversals. The maximum run, e.g. 7 bits, ensures that reversals occur frequently enough for self-clocking and the minimum run, e.g. 2 bits, ensures high density recording. RLL ensures that not too many ones or zeros fall in succession and to do this extra bits are added according to the formula chosen. The RLL technique provides improved reliability and increased recording density by up to 50 per cent compared with the MFM.

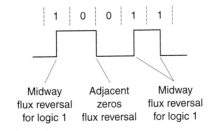

Figure 13.4   Modified FM (MFM) pulse sequence

Digital disks

Apart from the coding technique, disk capacity may also be increased by reducing the physical size of each cell thus increasing the number of cells per inch of track. As the cells get smaller and closer to each other, their magnetic fields get weaker with a relatively high level of noise resulting in a certain level of ambiguity in the logic level of the stored bit. To overcome this, each cell is sampled twice with the results fed into a 'peak-detecting' circuit to determine the actual logic level. However, disks with capacities of a few gigabytes have their cells so close to each other that they begin to overlap. This problem is resolved by a technique that was first developed by mathematicians working on space communications. It is a technique known as partial response maximum likelihood (PRML). In this technique, the analogue voltage induced in the read coil corresponding to the magnetic flux of each cell is converted into a 6-bit digital value. These digital values are then fed into a dedicated processor chip which by applying PRML determines the logic level of the cell. Disks using this technique are known as digital disk drives.

Disk organisation

The surface of the disk is divided into a number of concentric tracks as shown in Fig. 13.5. In addition, every track is divided into a number of sectors. Each sector is designed to hold 512 bytes. The tracks are numbered 0 onwards with track 0 at the outside, and the sectors are numbered 1 onwards.

The capacity of a disk may therefore be calculated as follows:

$$\text{capacity (bytes)} = \text{no. of tracks} \times \text{no. of sectors per track} \times 512 \times \text{no. of heads}$$

For a single-sided disk, the number of heads is one. In a double-sided (DS) disk, the number of heads is two. In the case of a hard disk where a number of disks are used, the number of heads is as stated by the manufacturer. For example, a double-sided floppy disk with 80 tracks and 18 sectors per track has a capacity of

$$\text{capacity} = 80 \times 18 \times 512 \times 2 = 1,474,560 \text{ bytes}$$

which is given the nominal value of 1.44MB.

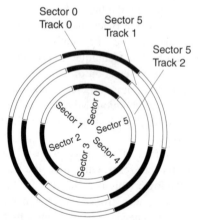

Sector 0
Track 0

Sector 5
Track 1

Sector 5
Track 2

Sector 0

Sector 1

Sector 2

Sector 3

Sector 4

Sector 5

Figure 13.5 Tracks and sectors

Formatting a disk

Before a disk can be used to store data, it has to be divided into designated tracks and sectors. This process is known as formatting a disk and is carried out by DOS command FORMAT D: where D: is the disk drive to be formatted.

In addition to dividing the disk into tracks and sectors, the format command tests the disk for bad sectors and ensures that they are not used, and creates a boot sector to track the sectors and tracks as they are used.

Data transfer rate and access time

The rate at which the data bits are transferred to or from the disk is known as the data transfer rate given in Kbits or Mbits per second, e.g. 500 Kbits/s for high density drives and 1 Mbit/s for extra high density drives.

Another important property of a disk drive is its access time. This is the time it takes the head to access a given sector in milliseconds. Because such a time depends on the original position of the head, the average access time is usually specified. Average access time is the time it takes the head to move half the width of the active part of the disk. Typical access times for floppy disk drives are 40–60 ms for older types and 15–20 ms for modern devices.

The floppy disk

Floppy disks use the MFM coding technique and thus are limited in their capacity. There are two types of floppy disks in common use in personal computers: the 5¼ inch and 3½ inch. The 5¼ inch type (Fig. 13.6) has a flexible protective jacket or sleeve. The centre of the disk is exposed to allow an adequate grip by the rotating spindle. A read/write longitudinal opening known as the aperture is provided to allow the head access to the tracks. The third opening allows access to a circular hole in the disk itself, known as the index hole, which provides a reference position for the drive. A write protect notch is provided on the sleeve which is normally left uncovered. When the notch is blocked by a piece of tape, a sensor, normally a photocoupler, sends a signal to the disk drive controller inhibiting all write operations. The disk is said to be write protected, i.e. its data may not be changed. The 5¼ inch floppies are available in 360KB DD (Double Density) and 1.2MB HD (High Density) capacities.

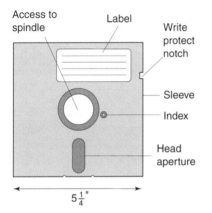

Figure 13.6 The 5¼ inch floppy disk

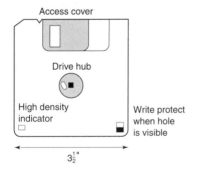

Figure 13.7 The 3½ inch floppy disk

The 3½ inch floppy disk (Fig. 13.7) has a rigid protective sleeve with no exposed parts. The disk is exposed to the read/write head only when it is inside the drive. A protective spring-loaded piece of metal slides away as the disk is pushed into the drive to expose the disk to the head. Write protect is effected by moving a plastic slider to reveal a hole in the bottom right corner of the sleeve. A similar sensor to the 5¼ inch disk drive is used to detect the presence of a hole except that normally the hole is covered to allow read and write operations. The 3½ inch disk is available in 720KB DD, 1.44MB HD and 2.88MB EHD (Extra High Density). High density disks are identified by another hole in the bottom right corner of the sleeve. A second sensor, normally a photocoupler, is used to recognise HD disks.

Table 13.1 lists the types of floppies stating their formatting specification.

Table 13.1

Floppy type	Capacity	No. of tracks	Sectors per track	Bytes per sector	Data rate
5¼ DS DD	360KB	40	9	512	250KB
5¼ DS HD	1.2MB	80	15	512	500KB
3½ DS DD	720KB	80	9	512	500KB
3½ DS HD	1.44MB	80	18	512	500KB
3½ DS EHD	2.88MB	80	36	512	1.0MB

Floppy disk operation The disk is made to rotate at a constant speed with a read/write head placed very close to the surface to capture the data stored in the cells or magnetise the cells into data bits. The close proximity of the head to the disk limits the speed of rotation of the disk to around 300 rpm (revolutions per minute). For single-sided (SS) disks only one head is necessary to access the cells. However, two heads are normally used for double-sided (DS) operations as shown in Fig. 13.8, one for each side. Incremental movement of the head from one track to the next is provided by a stepping motor.

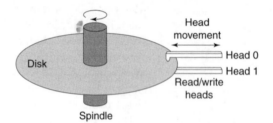

Figure 13.8 Double-sided disk

Fig. 13.9 shows the interface requirement of a floppy disk drive. The plastic floppy disk is inserted into the disk drive which is

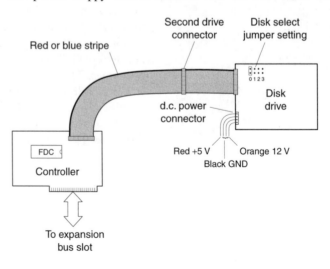

Figure 13.9 Floppy disk interface

2	Normal/high density
4	In use/head load
6	Drive select 3
8	Index
10	Drive select 0
12	Drive select 1
14	Drive select 2
16	Motor on
18	Direction select
20	STEP
22	Write data
24	Write enable
26	Track 00
28	Write protect
30	Read data
32	Side select
34	Disk change/ready

Odd pins are ground

Figure 13.10 Floppy connector pin-out

connected to the disk controller card via a flat 34-way ribbon cable. The controller card is inserted into an expansion slot on the motherboard. The cable carries both control and data signals from the motherboard to the disk drive. Pin 1 is identified by a red or blue stripe along one side. Care must be taken to ensure the correct orientation when the cable is connected to the controller card on one end and the disk drive on the other. Incorrect orientation will not damage any component but it will cause the drive indicator LED to be permanently on.

As can be seen from Fig. 13.10, the controller supports up to four floppy drives. Only two are normally used: drive select 0 (pin 10) for A: and drive select 1 (pin 12) for B:. The connector at the end of the cable must be connected to the drive designated as A:. If a second drive B: is used, then it must use the connector in the middle of the cable. Each drive must be configured to the correct drive number. This is carried out by jumper settings known as disk select DS0 to DS3, with DS0 for A: and DS1 for B:. To avoid having to configure the drive each time a new one is installed, the disk select jumpers are set by the manufacturer to second drive B:. A cable with control lines 10–16 twisted (Fig 13.11) will automatically provide the correct configuration. If a straight cable (a cable without a twist) is used, the DS setting must be changed.

Modern motherboards have on-board floppy disk controllers, in which case the cable will be plugged directly into connectors available on the motherboard. The on-board floppy disk controller may be disabled by the CMOS set-up to allow an expansion card controller to be used. Drive designations A: and B: may also be changed by modern CMOS set-up.

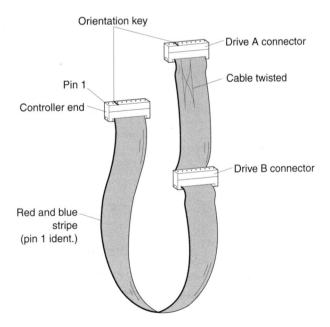

Figure 13.11 Disk cable with drive selection twist

Read/write operation

A floppy disk controller (FDC) 765 chip is used to process both control and data signals to and from the disk drive. When the computer receives a write to disk command, it activates the relevant routine in BIOS which sends coded digital signals to the FDC chip. The controller converts these digital signals into electrical signals which are used to control the drive. First the drive is selected by drive select 0, 1, 2 or 3 (pins 10, 12, 14 or 6). The relevant drive motor is then turned on by pin 16 (motor on). Two other signals determine the position of the head: the step (pin 20) provides a pulse to move the stepping motor one track forward or backward as determined by the voltage on pin 18 (direction select). The side select (pin 32) determines which of the two sides is to be addressed and the write data (pin 22) carries the actual data bits in the form of pulses to the head while pin 24 (write enable) protects the disk against accidental writing on the disk. Writing is inhibited when the write protect line (pin 28) is enabled by the write protect sensor. Pin 26 (track 00) is active when the head is on the outermost track of the disk, i.e. track 0, and the index (pin 8) provides a reference to determine the position of each bit on the track by sending a pulse to the controller every time the disk completes one revolution. The media type, i.e. normal or high density disk, is indicated by the status of pin 2.

In a read operation pins 22 and 24 are disabled and data is sent on pin 30 (read data) to the system memory where it is stored and made available for the computer to access as required. Once loaded into memory, access to this data is not slowed down by the relatively long access time of the disk drive. However, if the disk is removed and another disk is inserted into the drive, the new disk must be re-read. To ensure this happens, pin 34 (disk change) is enabled by a small solenoid sensor every time a disk is removed.

The hard disk

The hard disk consists of a number of rigid disks known as platters made of aluminium covered with a thin layer of magnetic coating (Fig. 13.12) and placed in a sealed container. A separate read/write head is provided for each active disk surface. Each surface is formatted into a number of tracks known as cylinders and each cylinder is in turn divided into a number of sectors, as is the case with the floppy disk (Fig. 13.13). The storage capacity of a hard disk may then be calculated as follows:

$$\text{capacity (bytes)} = \text{no. of tracks per disk surface} \times \text{no. of sectors per track} \times \text{no. of heads} \times 512$$

The disks rotate at a high angular velocity of between 5400 and 7200 rpm, which improves the access time compared with the floppy drive. The sealed container keeps dust etc. away from the surface of the platters allowing the head to fly very close to the disk surface, which increases the potential storage capacity of the drive.

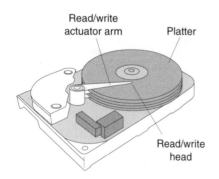

Read/write actuator arm   Platter

Read/write head

Figure 13.12 The hard disk

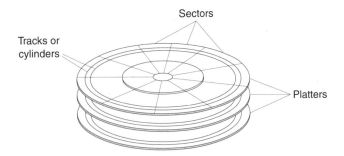

Figure 13.13 Hard disk platters

Types of hard disk drives

Early hard disk drives such as the ST506, now obsolete, were 'dumb' drives in that they required a separate controller card to manage data conversion and exchange between the drive and the PC. Later drives such as the IDE placed the controller on the drive itself, had increased capacities and faster rates of data transfer using fast PCI or VESA local buses.

The ST506

The ST506 which was developed by Shugart (now Seagate Technologies) in 1980 had a capacity of 5MB employing MFM coding. Higher capacities (up to 20MB) were obtained with RLL coding. The ST506 drive required a separate controller card which was slotted into an ISA expansion bus on the motherboard. Two, separate, flat ribbon cables were necessary to connect the controller to the drive: a 34-way control and 20-way data cables (Fig. 13.14).

As can be seen from Fig. 13.14, two separate drives may be supported by a single controller. Each drive has its own data cable

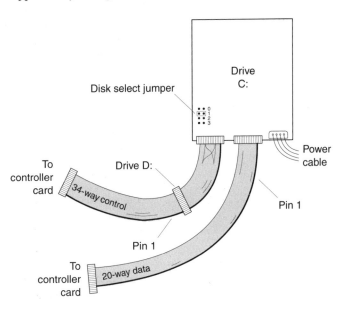

Figure 13.14 Connecting the ST506 controller card

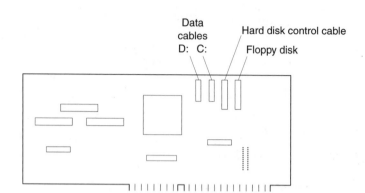

Data
cables
D: C:

Hard disk control cable

Floppy disk

Figure 13.15 The ST506 controller card

but shares the same control cable with drive C: connected at the end connector and D: at the middle connector. A drive is designated either C: (first drive) or D: (second drive) by the disk select (DS) jumper setting assigned in the same way as in the floppy disk drive. A twist in the control cable may also be used to assign the drive letter as shown in the diagram. Compared with the floppy cable, the hard disk control cable has fewer twisted lines. Typical connector pin arrangements on a controller card serving both floppy and hard disk drives are shown in Fig. 13.15.

Apart from its low capacity, the ST506 suffers from a low data transfer rate of between 2 and 3 Mbits/s caused by the slow 8-bit ISA expansion bus.

The ESDI standard

Based on the new protocol for data exchange between the PC and a hard drive known as the ATA (AT Attachment) specifications, the integrated small device interface (ESDI) standard is an improved version of the ST506. The ESDI has a maximum capacity 1GB and a data transfer rate of up to 2 Mbits/s. It retained the two cable connections to a controller card making it fully compatible with the ST506 drive.

The IDE standard

The integrated device electronics (IDE) standard is another ATA-based standard for hard disks. Unlike the ESDI, however, it is not compatible with the early ST506. Its main innovation is, as its name suggests, the integration of the controller functions onto the disk drive itself. This made it possible for drive manufacturers to enhance the performance of the drive independently of the PC. With data interpretation and transfer functions carried out on-board the drive, connection to the PC is reduced to a simple interface card slotted into an ISA expansion bus on the motherboard. Another main

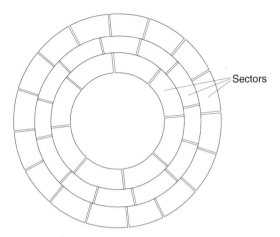

Figure 13.16   Zoned recording

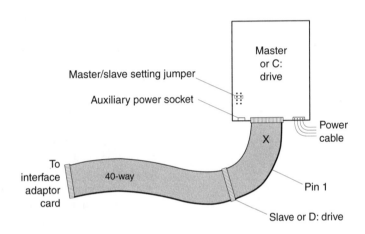

Figure 13.17   The IDE adaptor card

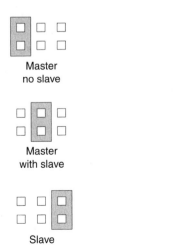

Figure 13.18   Master/slave jumper selection

feature of the IDE drive is its ability to increase the number of sectors on the outer tracks, a technique known as zoned recording, thus increasing the storage capacity of the disk (Fig. 13.16).

IDE is designed to support up to two independent hard disk drives, each with a maximum capacity of 528MB and a transfer rate of 7 Mbits/s. The two drives known as master (drive C:) and slave (drive D:) are served by a single 40-way ribbon cable (Fig. 13.17). Unlike the ST506 drives which are identifiable by the drive adaptor card, and are therefore addressed separately by the PC, each IDE drive has its own controller built onto the drive itself. As far as the PC is concerned, the two drives look identical. System BIOS is made aware of the master/slave arrangements by a signal on the DASP (Drive Active/Slave Present) pin 39 which is asserted by the jumper settings shown in Fig. 13.18. Three settings are possible: master no slave; master/slave; and slave.

Disk capacity constraints

When the computer wishes to access a disk drive, it asserts INT13 which calls and runs a handler routine contained in ROM BIOS. This routine specifies the cylinder, the head and the sector which is to be accessed, a technique known as cylinder/head/sector (CHS) addressing. BIOS software is designed to handle a maximum of 1024 cylinders, 255 heads and 63 sectors per track. This provides a potentially huge disk capacity of 8.4GB. However, the maximum capacity of an IDE drive is constrained by another specification, namely the ATA specifications. ATA supports a maximum of 65,536 cylinders, 16 heads and 255 sectors per track giving a potential capacity of 136.9GB. When both sets of restrictions are combined (1024 cylinders, 16 heads and 63 sectors per track) the potential disk capacity is reduced to $1024 \times 16 \times 63 \times 512 = 528$ million bytes or 504MB. This is known as the 504MB limit.

The EIDE standard

The enhanced IDE (EIDE) standard is devised to overcome the constraint that ATA placed upon IDE drives while maintaining backward compatibility. EIDE supports up to four drives with a maximum storage capacity of 8.4GB each and data transfer rates up to 13.3 Mbits/s. A further innovation of the EIDE is its ability to support a CD-ROM and a tape streamer as well as a hard disk drive. This is made possible by using an extended ATA protocol called the ATAPI (AT Attachment Packet Interface) with extra commands for the operation of non-disk drives. The ATAPI protocol contains several new commands which are specific to CD-ROM and tape peripherals.

Increased disk capacity beyond the 504MB limit of the IDE standard is achieved by enhanced BIOS software which abandons the CHS approach to accessing the drive. Instead, each sector is assigned a 28-bit address known as a logical block address (LBA). This provides for $10^{28} = 268,435,456$ sectors. With each sector having a capacity of 512 bytes, the maximum disk capacity available under LBA is 128GB. The logical block address of each sector must be translated into a CHS count which is necessary to enable DOS to access the drive. As a result, the limit to disk capacity is now set by the limitations placed by BIOS on the number of cylinders, heads and sectors per track, namely 8GB.

LBA is the standard method of addressing disks with capacities in excess of half a gigabyte. Another technique known as enhanced CHS (ECHS) translates the actual CHS count into another count which is acceptable to the operating system. For example, a drive with 2000 cylinders and 16 heads is translated into a drive with 1000 cylinders and 32 heads.

LBA or ECHS must be enabled in CMOS set-up when drives with a capacity greater than 504MB are installed.

Data transfer

The most significant benefit of EIDE is its greatly improved data transfer rate compared with the standard ATA. EIDE is able to do this in two ways: programmed input/output (PIO) and DMA. In the PIO mode, EIDE takes control of the bus from the processor by invoking the I/O channel ready control signal to regulate the flow of data. The drive can then establish the best transfer rate using the increased bandwidth and higher frequency of the PCI or VESA expansion slots. Transfer rates of 11.1 Mbits/s (mode 3) and 16.6 Mbits/s (mode 4) are possible. Developments have taken place for transferring data using DMA. Unlike the PIO techniques, the DMA transfer takes place without the intervention of the processor. However, this technique requires substantial changes in the BIOS software and new device drivers.

The EIDE interface

EIDE provides for two interface channels: a primary channel supporting two separate hard disk drives and a secondary channel to support CD-ROM and tape drives. The primary channel is usually connected to a fast local bus (a PCI or VESA). To ensure backward compatibility, the same IRQ and address setting as those for IDE are used.

The SCSI bus Pronounced 'scuzzy', the small computer systems interface (SCSI) is a bus which controls the flow of data between the computer and several peripherals. The peripherals are connected to a SCSI host adaptor on the motherboard by a multi-way cable as shown in Fig. 13.19. Each device (including the host) is identified by an individual ID number or address asigned to it when it is connected to the bus.

SCSI is an intelligent bus which works by using a command set to negotiate data transfer between a peripheral and the host computer.

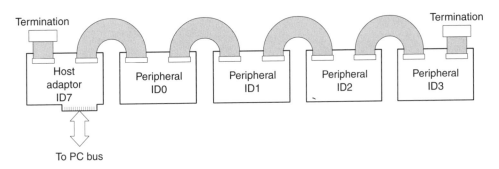

Figure 13.19 The SCSI bus connection

When the host computer wishes to transfer data, the host adaptor takes on the role of the 'initiator' and negotiates for control of the bus. The initiator identifies the 'target' device, e.g. a disk drive, which takes control of the transfer of data. The SCSI standard allows for several initiators on the bus.

The original standard SCSI-1 supports eight devices numbered 0 to 7 and connected via a 50-way cable as shown in Fig. 13.19. All the devices connected to the SCSI bus function independently of the others under the control of the host adaptor card. The host adaptor which is usually slotted into a fast PCI or VESA local bus slot is given ID number 7. The system boots up from ID0 which is usually occupied by the master hard disk drive. Both ends of the bus chain must be terminated with a set of resistors to prevent signal reflections and ensure data integrity along the cable. Most SCSI adaptors feature an internal 50-way ribbon cable connector for devices placed within the system unit, such as a master hard disk drive or a CD-ROM drive, and an external 50-way cable connector for external devices such as a scanner or CD recorder (Fig. 13.20).

The original SCSI-1 used asynchronous data transfer in which data was exchanged a byte at a time at a rate of up to 3 Mbits/s. Asynchronous transfer was introduced with SCSI-2 which increased the transfer rate to 10 Mbits/s. SCSI-2, using 68-way ribbon cable, introduced a new standard which included the broadening of the data width to 16 and 32 bits, known as wide SCSI-2. For instance, a fast wide SCSI-2 supports 16 devices and provides a transfer rate of 20 Mbits/s.

Ultra SCSI adaptors further increased data throughput to 40 Mbits/s. Recent introductions of plug and play SCAM (SCSI configured automatically) adaptors can automatically set the IDs of devices to avoid conflicts.

Installing a SCSI adaptor card involves allocating an IRQ number and an I/O port address range which are not used by other peripherals. The allocation is carried out by jumper settings on the card.

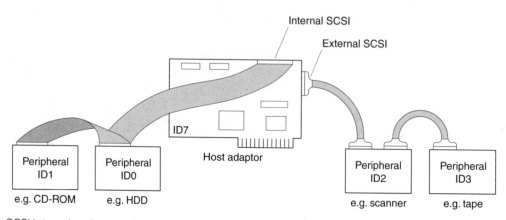

Figure 13.20 SCSI internal and external connections

Before the SCSI is used, the appropriate software routines provided by the manufacturer must be loaded. A subdirectory, normally called SCSI, is created in which all relevant files and routines are stored. Furthermore, two device drivers have to be installed in CONFIG.SYS: one for the host adaptor card and the other for the peripheral device, in this case the hard disk. Both drivers are provided by the manufacturer. A typical device driver for the host adaptor is

DEVICE = C:\SCSI\ASPI2DOS.SYS

and a typical device driver for the SCSI hard disk:

DEVICE = C:\SCSI\DISK.SYS

where DISK.SYS is the SCSI hard disk driver.

Formatting the hard disk

Unlike floppy disks, modern hard disks (IDE, EIDE and SCSI) have their recording surface divided into tracks and sectors by the manufacturer. This process is known as low level formatting and requires a special routine. Manufacturers strongly advise against low level formatting a hard disk and for this reason low level formatting programs are not available as a standard in MS-DOS. However, before a new hard disk can be used, it must first be partitioned into logical drives and then each drive must be formatted with the FORMAT command which carries out what is known as high level formatting of the disk.

Partitioning a hard disk is carried out by DOS's FDISK command which generates a menu allowing the user to divide the hard disk into one or more partitions known as logical drives such as C:, D:, E: and so on. Each partition is allocated a proportion of the total disk space. The partition where the operating system is to be loaded, normally logical drive C:, must be made active. Failure to do so will result in the system's BIOS being unable to detect and load the operating system on start-up. For SCSI disk drives, partitioning is carried out by a special routine, AFDISK.EXE, which is provided by the manufacturer.

Following partitioning, each partition must be formatted. MS-DOS's FORMAT command is used for this purpose and carries out a high level format of each logical drive separately. High level formatting does not destroy the original data on the disk; it merely erases the logical structure of the partition. The original data may be recovered by such commands as UNFORMAT and MIRROR. However, if the original files were scattered over a number of sectors on the surface of the disk, it might be difficult or impossible to recover all lost data. Obviously, if the original data has been overwritten by new data, it is lost for ever.

Before partitioning or formatting a hard disk, it is advisable to copy all files including the system and DOS files (especially FDISK and FORMAT) to ensure that data is not lost and that the system may be reloaded onto the newly partitioned hard disk.

Clusters

For the purposes of storing files on a disk, DOS divides the disk space into clusters. A standard cluster occupies eight sectors giving a cluster size of

$$8 \times \text{sector size} = 8 \times 512 = 4096 \text{ bytes}$$

Each cluster is identified by an entry in a file allocation table (FAT) on the disk. Files are then stored into clusters with the FAT keeping a record of which clusters belong to which file. The size of the FAT and that of each cluster thus determine the maximum size of a drive that may be addressed by the FAT. Versions of DOS prior to 4.0 used a 12-bit entry to indentify each cluster, thus limiting the number of entries to $2^{12} = 4096$. With a cluster size of 8192 bytes, the maximum addressable disk size was $4096 \times 8192 = 33,554,432$ or 32MB. Version 5.0 increased the number of entries into the FAT to 65,536, thus increasing disk size to 134,217,728 or 128MB. Further increases in potential size, to say 512MB, may be produced by doubling the size of the cluster.

Increasing cluster size is very wasteful of disk space. This is because a file must occupy one complete cluster regardless of how small it is. What is left of the cluster cannot be used by another file. Large files which occupy a number of clusters may also leave parts of a cluster unused, which remain empty. On average, each file on the disk wastes half a cluster. Large size clusters therefore result in greater waste in disk capacity. For this reason DOS version 6 is designed to use the smallest possible cluster size for a disk with a given capacity. Disks with capacities of 1GB or over are partitioned into 0.5GB sections.

Optimisation of a hard disk

There are several ways of optimising the operation of a given hard disk. These include the use of the following routines: DEFRAG, SCANDISK, SMARTDRV.

DEFRAG

When files are written to a disk, they are stored in contiguous cluster locations, i.e. end to end. The next file to be written is stored in the locations immediately following the previous file. If one of the files is expanded following some modification, it will no longer fit into the space allocated for it and new uncontiguous cluster locations are used. Over time, files will be fragmented all over the storage space of the disk. The result is that data retrieval becomes extremely slow as the head jumps between vastly separated locations. The DEFRAG utility provided by DOS rearranges the storage of files on the disk. DEFRAG scans the directory and FAT entries to determine which files are fragmented and proceeds to rewrite the files in contiguous locations. The process of scanning the disk identifies bad sectors and ensures that they are not used. The whole process of defragmentation is displayed on the screen as it takes place.

SCANDISK

SCANDISK is a very powerful tool introduced by DOS versions 6.x onwards to replace CHEDSK and RECOVER commands in previous DOS versions. SCANDISK scans the disk for bad and 'lost' sectors. When bad sectors are identified, SCANDISK ensures that the clusters containing them are not used by marking them bad in the FAT. When 'lost' clusters are found, SCANDISK prompts the user to indicate whether the data contained in these clusters is to be saved. If the answer is yes, the SCANDISK routine proceeds to convert the lost clusters to files with filenames such as FILE0000.CHK and stores them in the root directory.

SMARTDRV

In spite of great improvements in the data transfer rate of hard disks, they remain slow in comparison with the CPU and system memory. SMARTDRV is a DOS routine which decreases the time the CPU spends reading data from the hard disk, thus effectively increasing its data transfer rate. SMARTDRV is a disk-caching routine which reserves an area in extended memory, i.e. cache memory, in which it stores the data it reads from the disk. This data may then be accessed directly by an application program faster than it can access the same information on the hard disk. The disk cache memory may also be used to store data temporarily before it is written to the hard disk. This data is subsequently sent to the hard disk when the CPU has time between its different tasks, which improves the general performance of the system.

To run the smartdrive routine, SMARTDRV must be specified in AUTOEXEC.BAT normally as follows:

```
C:\DOS\SMARTDRV.EXE
```

For Windows 3.1 onwards, disk caching routines are automatically included when the program is installed.

Virtual disk A virtual disk, also known as a RAM disk or drive, is an area of system memory that is treated by the computer as another disk drive. It has the advantage of being very fast and the disadvantage of occupying a part of extended memory.

A virtual drive may be defined by a device driver in CONFIG.SYS which takes the form of

DEVICE=C:\DOS\RAMDRIVE.SYS size sector directory/e

where size specifies the size of the RAM drive in KB, sector specifies the size of each sector in bytes, directory specifies the maximum number of directory entries and /e tells DOS to use extended memory. To define a 128KB RAM disk with 256-byte sectors and 64 possible directory entries, the following should be entered in CONFIG.SYS:

DEVICE=C:\DOS\RAMDRIVE.SYS 128 256 64

It is not usual to use both RAMDRIVE and SMARTDRV at the same time.

Comparison of PC storage facilities

Table 13.2 shows how the various storage facilities available for a PC compare with each other.

Table 13.2

Storage type	Bus speed (MHz)	Bus width (bits)	Size	Access time	Transfer rate (Mbits/s)
CPU on-chip cache	75–200	32	8–16KB	5–10 ns	300–666
External cache (SRAM)	33–66	32, 64	256KB–1MB	15 ns	133–528
Main memory (DRAM)	33–66	32, 64	8–256MB	60 ns	66–264
Hard disk	8–33	16, 32	500MB–4GB	10–20 ms	1–8

14 Monitors and video adaptors

The video display unit (VDU) is one of the two principal interfaces between the user and the computer, the other being the keyboard. Originally employed for monochrome (black and white) character-based texts, modern video displays can provide colour texts and 2-D and 3-D colour graphics with very fast response time. The performance of the video system is today as important as that of the PC itself.

The heart of the display system is the video adaptor card which slots into a PC expansion slot (Fig. 14.1). The video adaptor translates text and graphics instructions into video signals which are fed to the monitor for display. Two types of monitors are in common use in PCs: the raster or CRT (Cathode Ray Tube) and the LCD (Liquid Crystal Display).

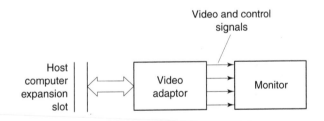

Figure 14.1 Video adapter card

The CRT monitor

The CRT operates on the same principle as the old thermionic valve, i.e. a negatively charged hot cathode emits electrons which are attracted to and collected by a positively charged anode.

In the CRT, high speed electrons are emitted by an electron gun (Fig. 14.2). They are focused and accelerated by an electron lens and directed towards the screen which acts as the positively charged anode. The inside of the screen consists of a large number of very small dots known as pixels which are coated with a fluorescent powder or phosphor which gives off a visible glow when hit by the high speed stream of electrons known as the electron beam. When the electron beam is turned off, the glow quickly fades away. The electron beam generated by the electron gun gives a stationary dot

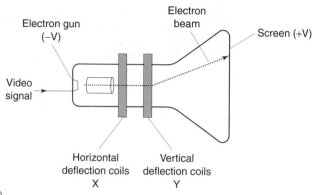

Figure 14.2 The cathode ray tube (CRT)

on the screen. In order to produce a display, the CRT must have the capacity to deflect the beam in both the horizontal and vertical directions, X and Y. Computer monitors use electromagnetic deflection in which two pairs of deflecting coils (X and Y), also known as scanning coils, are placed at right angles to each other along the neck of the tube. When current passes through the X and Y coils, a magnetic field is created which deflects the beam in the horizontal and vertical directions respectively.

A continuous display is created by refreshing the screen, i.e. recreating the image at regular intervals. Each complete scan of the screen is known as a frame. A refresh rate (i.e. a frame frequency) of between 50 and 90 Hz is normally used. Refreshing the screen involves driving the electron beam across the screen from left to right in a series of hundreds of lines as shown in Fig. 14.3. This process, known as scanning of the screen, is carried out by applying a timebase waveform (Fig. 14.4) to the X coils causing the beam to travel from left to right at a steady speed (the sweep) and then to return very quickly back to the left of the screen (the flyback) and so on. The path of the beam, i.e. the line scans, is known as the raster. At the same time, the beam is made to travel downward (vertical sweep) at a constant but slower rate (a frame or field frequency of between 50 and 90 Hz) to produce a scan of the entire screen. At the end of the scan, the beam is made to return quickly (vertical flyback) to its original position ready to scan the next frame and so on. During both the line and frame flyback, the electron beam is turned off to avoid the flyback retrace lines appearing on the screen.

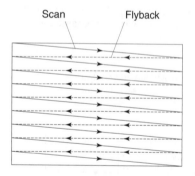

Figure 14.3 Video scanning

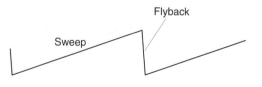

Figure 14.4 The timebase waveform

Interlacing Where the refresh rate is low, the process of scanning complete displays may introduce flicker caused by the comparatively long period of time it takes to complete a scan. This is avoided by a technique known as interlacing. Interlace scanning involves scanning the 'odd' lines 1, 3, 5, etc., first followed by the 'even' lines 2, 4, 6, etc. Only one-half, known as the field, of the display is therefore scanned each time. Unlike television receivers where the refresh rate is low (25 pictures per second), interlacing is not essential for computer monitors.

Display quality As the electron beam scans the surface of the CRT screen, its intensity (i.e. strength) is varied by applying a video signal to the electron gun, a process known as modulating the electron beam. The strength of the electron beam determines the brightness of each dot or pixel as each line is scanned. The quality of the display is determined by the number of pixels that are available to be scanned by the electron beam. For high quality graphics, a large number of pixels must be made available to enable fine details to be reproduced on the screen. A second factor which determines the quality of the video display is the distance between the pixels, known as the dot pitch, given in millimetres. The nearer the pixels are to each other, i.e. the smaller the pitch, the higher is the image quality. For a standard quality graphic display, a dot pitch of 0.28 mm is considered adequate. Professional standard graphic displays require a tube with a pitch of 0.25 mm or less.

Resolution and sharpness The resolution of a monitor is the total number of pixels available on the screen given as

horizontal pixels × vertical pixels

For example, a monitor with 640 pixels per line (horizontal) and 480 lines (vertical) has a resolution of 640 × 480.

While the resolution (total number of pixels) of the screen determines the amount of video information that the image contains, i.e. its physical quality, its sharpness is determined by the dot pitch.

For a text display, the resolution is given as

number of columns × number of rows

For example, a screen which accommodates 40 characters per row (columns) and 25 characters down (rows) has a resolution of 40 × 25.

Resolution, pitch and screen size Like the domestic television receiver, a monitor has an aspect ratio (width:height) of 4:3 (Fig. 14.5). The size of the monitor, which is usually given in inches, refers to the diagonal measurement of the

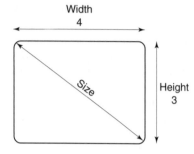

Figure 14.5 Aspect ratio

screen. Thus a 14-inch monitor has a width of 11.2 inches and a height of 8.4 inches.

Given a dot pitch of, say, 0.28 mm and a screen size of, say, 14 inches, the total number of pixels, i.e. the screen resolution, may be calculated as follows:

A 14-inch screen with an aspect ratio of 4:3 gives
a screen width = 11.2 inches = 284.48 mm and
a screen height = 8.4 inches = 213.36 mm

If the distance between each pixel (dot pitch) = 0.28 mm, then

the number of horizontal pixels = $\frac{284.48}{0.28}$ = 1016

the number of vertical pixels = $\frac{231.36}{0.28}$ = 826

giving a resolution of 1016 × 826.

In practice, this screen will be said to support a standard resolution of 1024 × 768.

Monitor signal requirements

Fig. 14.6 shows a block diagram for a monochrome CRT display unit. As can be seen, three different signals are necessary for the construction of an image on the screen of a CRT: the video signal, a horizontal synchronising pulse, H sync, and a vertical synchronising pulse, V sync. The video signal which is amplified before it is fed into the cathode of the CRT modulates the electron beam to produce different pixel brightnesses as it scans the screen line by line. The two synchronising pulses, a horizontal (line) H sync pulse and a vertical (frame) V sync pulse, are used to ensure that the screen scan is in sync with the video signal. The two sync pulses are used to trigger their respective oscillators which generate the appropriate deflecting waveforms. These waveforms are amplified by a driver power stage and fed into the appropriate deflecting coils. The line driver stage, known as the line output amplifier, also feeds the extra high tension (EHT) stage which provides the 10 to 30 kV necessary for the final anode of the tube.

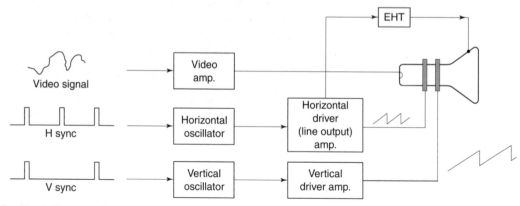

Figure 14.6 Block diagram of a monochrome video display unit

TTL and analogue monitors

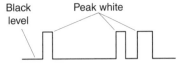

Figure 14.7 TTL video waveform

There are two ways in which the electron beam may be modulated by the video signal: digital, also known as TTL, and analogue.

In its basic form, the video signal to a digital or TTL monitor can take one of two states: logic HIGH which turns the electron beam ON or logic LOW which turns the electron beam OFF. A pixel may be at peak white (ON) or at black level (OFF) (Fig. 14.7). To produce other shades, a second digital input known as intensity, I, is sent to the monitor, in which case $2^2 = 4$ different shades may be produced: peak white, light grey, dark grey and black (Table 14.1).

Table 14.1

TTL video	Intensity, I	Pixel
0	0	Peak white
0	1	Light grey
1	0	Dark grey
1	1	Black

In the analogue-type monitor, as the video signal is analogue it may therefore hold an infinite number of values resulting in an infinite number of shades between peak white and black (Fig. 14.8).

Colour monitors

In the colour CRT, three independent electron guns are used, one for each primary colour: red, green and blue (RGB). On the screen, colour is created by focusing each gun on a specially coated dot which when hit by a fast electron emits a primary colour. Colours are created by mixing the red, green and blue components in different proportions. Table 14.2 shows the general rules of colour mixing.

Table 14.2

R + G = yellow
R + B = magenta
B + G = cyan
R + G + B = white

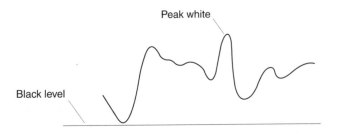

Figure 14.8 Analogue video signal

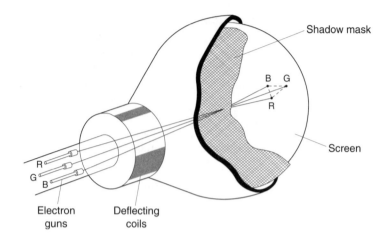

Figure 14.9 The shadow mask tube

Theoretically, an infinite number of colours may be created by the addition of appropriate quantities of the three primary colours. However, the actual number of different colours that are available in a video system is determined by the mode of operation of the video adaptor and the type of monitor used.

The shadow mask colour tube

In the shadow mask tube, the three guns are mounted at 120° to each other as shown in Fig. 14.9. The guns are tilted by a small amount towards the central axis of the tube so that their electron beams converge and cross the shadow mask passing through carefully positioned holes to strike their respective dots. A large number of electrons miss their holes and are lost through hitting the mask itself, resulting in low efficiency and low brightness. The dots are arranged to form a regular system of triangles known as triads (Fig. 14.10) which form a single pixel. The dots within each pixel are indistinguishable to the naked eye which sees the three primary colours mixed together. By modulating each electron beam independently, different combinations of intensities of R, G and B are obtained and a large number of colours may thus be recreated on the screen.

The pitch of a colour tube is given by the shortest distance between two dots of the same primary colour.

Figure 14.10 RGB triad pixel

Character generation

The video system may be programmed to operate in two different modes: text mode and graphic mode. In the graphic mode, each pixel is individually addressed by the adaptor to determine its attributes, i.e. its characteristics in terms of brightness and colour. In the text mode, text characters are allocated a matrix of pixels, e.g. 5×7 or 7×11. A character is displayed on the screen by the electron beam

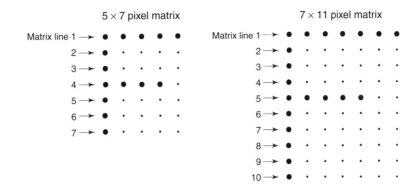

Figure 14.11 5 × 7 and 7 × 11 matrix displays

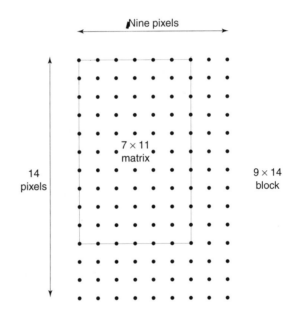

Figure 14.12 7 × 11 matrix block

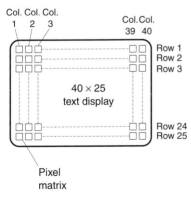

Figure 14.13 40 × 25 text display

scanning the matrix and energising the appropriate pixels, line by line, as shown in Fig. 14.11.

As characters are separated by a few pixels from each other, and rows of characters are separated by a few scanlines, the complete pixel block is larger than the pixel matrix itself, e.g. 9 × 14 for a pixel matrix of 7 × 11 as shown in Fig. 14.12. In the text mode the screen is divided into columns and rows to accommodate the designated format which specifies the number of characters per row and the number of rows on the screen. Fig. 14.13 shows a 40 × 25 (40 characters across × 25 rows) text screen format.

Assuming a 5 × 7 dot or pixel format, a row of characters then occupies seven pixel lines. The process of scanning involves the electron beam sweeping across the first pixel line of all the characters in the first row energising the appropriate dots along that line scan. This is then followed by pixel line 2 and so on. The video signal thus consists of a series of dot patterns (also known as bit

Line scan
dot pattern

	(V)	(F)
Pixel line 1 →	10001	11111
2 →	10001	10000
3 →	10001	10000
4 →	10001	11100
5 →	10001	10000
6 →	01010	10000
7 →	00100	10000

Space

Figure 14.14 Pixel line dot pattern for characters VF

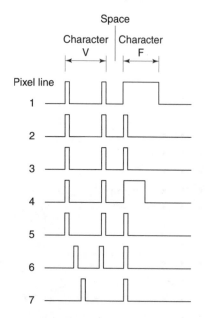

Figure 14.15 Pixel line signals for characters VF

patterns) corresponding to the first pixel line of each successive character, followed by the dot patterns of the second pixel line of the same characters and so on up to the seventh. Following a few blank scanlines, the process is then repeated for the second row of characters.

If, for example, V and F (Fig. 14.14) are the first two characters in a row, then the video signals for each of the seven scanlines are as shown in Fig. 14.15. These video signals are generated using the arrangement shown in Fig. 14.16. The character generator is a look-up ROM chip which contains the dot patterns of every character. When the ASCII code is fed into the ROM character generator, the dot pattern of that character appears at the output of the chip, pixel line by pixel line. The pixel line is selected by the select address. For instance, assuming that characters V and F in Fig. 14.14 are to be displayed, then the ASCII code for the first character, V, is fed to the character generator while simultaneously 000 is placed on the select address to select the first pixel line. The character generator will then produce the dot pattern of the first pixel line of V, namely 10001. This parallel output is then converted into a serial signal using a simple parallel-in serial-out (PISO) shift register to form the first part of the first video line. The ASCII code input then switches to the next character, F. With the select address remaining at 000, the dot pattern of the first pixel line of the second character, 11111, is produced and applied to the shift register to form the second part of the first video line and so on for all other characters along the first row. At the start of the second line scan, the ASCII code input reverts back to the first character V, but this time the scanline

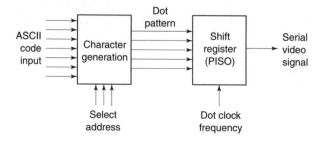

Figure 14.16 Video generation

address is incremented to 001 to select the dot pattern of the second pixel line and so on.

Interlacing

With interlacing, each complete picture is composed of two fields: an odd field scanning odd lines only and an even field scanning even lines only. When characters are displayed, each matrix pixel line is repeated, the first time in the 'odd' field and the second time in the 'even' field. Each matrix pixel line thus occupies two line scans giving a total of 14 lines per character for a 7×5 matrix (or 20 lines if spaces between display lines are included).

Memory mapping

As explained earlier, the electron beam repeatedly scans the CRT screen to produce a steady and continuous display, a process known as refreshing the screen. For this to take place, the contents of the displayed image must be retained in memory, character by character for text mode and pixel by pixel for graphic mode. This technique is known as memory mapping. Since the contents of the displayed image may be changed, volatile memory is used which is known as display or video RAM. Refreshing the screen thus becomes a matter of reading the contents of video RAM to retrace the display over and over again.

In the text mode in which the screen is divided into a number of character blocks, e.g. 40×25 or 80×25, memory mapping involves allocating one memory location, i.e. 1 byte, to each block where the ASCII code of the character is entered. This is known as character mapping. A second adjacent memory location is allocated to define special display qualities for the displayed character, known as attributes, such as blinking, underlining, intensity and reverse video as well as background and foreground colour (Fig. 14.17). In colour applications, the first half of the attribute byte (the most significant nibble) provides information about the colour of the character itself. The least significant nibble provides the background colour code. Since 4 bits are used, $2^4 = 16$ different colours may thus be displayed: 16 colours each for the foreground and the background of the character block.

In the graphic mode, each individual pixel is allocated one or more bits in one or more memory locations. The bits provide coded information on the intensity and other attributes of the particular pixel. This technique is known as all-points addressable (APA). It is also known as bit-map graphic. In the case of colour, a pixel is a three-dot RGB triad. Each dot is allocated memory space to describe its intensity. The relative intensities of the three dots define the colour of the pixel.

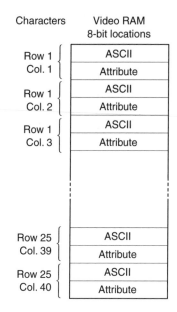

Figure 14.17 The allocation of memory space for a 40 × 25 text display

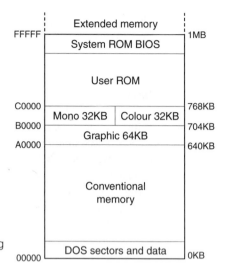

Figure 14.18   PC memory map showing
the video memory space

DOS video architecture   DOS allocates the first 128KB of upper memory for video RAM
(Fig. 14.18). The first 64KB (A0000H to AFFFFH) is allocated for
graphic mode video, the next 32KB (B0000H to B7FFF) is allocated
for monochrome and the last 32KB (B8000H to BFFFFH) is
allocated for colour video text mode. When used in the graphic
mode, the whole of the 128KB may be utilised.

The video adaptor – text mode   Fig. 14.19 shows a block diagram for a basic text mode video
adaptor. At the heart of the adaptor card is the cathode ray tube
controller (CRTC) such as the 6845. The CRTC is a highly
integrated programmable chip which keeps track of the position of

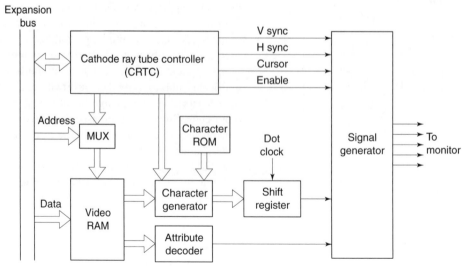

Figure 14.19   The text mode video adaptor block diagram

the beam, provides a sequence of character addresses to video RAM and instructs the character generator to produce the dot patterns for each line scan. The character ROM holds the pixel patterns for all ASCII characters. The character generator converts these patterns into the appropriate dot patterns for the selected screen format, font and interlace as determined by the CRTC. The CRTC also generates the line and field sync pulses as well a cursor output which, together with the dot patterns and the attribute signals, are fed into the signal generator which generates the necessary signals to the monitor.

A master oscillator (crystal controlled or phase-locked loop (PLL) is used to provide the 'dot clock' which determines the rate at which successive dots are energised. Other clock pulses including the sync and blanking pulses are then derived by subdividing the master dot clock.

The contents of the display can be changed by the CPU writing the ASCII code of the new character and its attributes in the memory locations determined by the position on the screen. The block diagram (Fig. 14.19) shows a multiplexer (MUX) which provides the CPU with access to the video RAM. This method slows the process of updating the display if the location it wishes to write to is simultaneously being read by the CRTC. In this case, the CPU may have to introduce a number of wait states. To avoid this, a dual-port RAM (VRAM) is used which provides two sets of data ports: one set for reading and a second for writing.

The CRTC may be programmed for pixel matrix size, font (i.e. shape of character), number of colours and interlacing as well as text/graphic mode. This may be carried out using the PC's system BIOS routines. However, the need for complex routines to configure advanced colour and graphic displays has resulted in the incorporation of a video BIOS ROM chip on the adaptor card itself. PC DOS architecture provides 128KB (C0000H to DFFFFH) of system memory for expansion. ROM BIOS applications and video BIOS will be loaded within that space.

Bandwidth and dot frequency

The actual dot frequency depends on the format, resolution and refresh rate of the display. For example, given a resolution of 640 × 480, then

Total number of pixels = 680 × 480 = 326,400

And if the refresh rate is 60 Hz, then

Dot clock frequency (pixels per second)
= 326,400 × 60 = 19,584,000 Hz = 19.584 MHz

Assuming that the flyback (horizontal and vertical) occupies 25 per cent of the time, the dot frequency will increase by

19.584 × 0.25 = 4.896 MHz

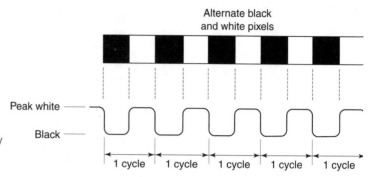

Figure 14.20 Maximum video frequency is produced with alternate black and white pixel display

giving a dot frequency of

$19.584 + 4.896 = 24.48$ MHz

A more precise calculation may be made if the line and field flyback times are known.

The dot clock frequency is normally (and erroneously) referred to as the bandwidth of the video system. IBM, for instance, specifies 25 MHz as the bandwidth for the 680×480 resolution display considered above.

The actual bandwidth, however, is half the dot frequency. Bandwidth is the maximum frequency of the system, and in the case of a video system it determines the bandwidth of the video amplifier. Maximum video frequency is obtained when adjacent pixels are alternately at maximum and minimum intensities, e.g. black and white for a monochrome display. When the electron beam scans a line containing a sequence of alternate black and white pixels, the video waveform is that shown in Fig. 14.20. As can be seen, for any adjacent pair of black and white pixels, one complete cycle is obtained. Hence for the 10 pixels shown, five cycles are produced. It follows that for a complete display of alternate black and white pixels, the number of cycles required is half the total number of pixels. This gives a maximum frequency or bandwidth of ½ × dot clock frequency.

Memory requirements – text mode

In the text mode, each character is allocated 2 bytes, one byte for the ASCII code and another for the attributes. The number of bytes and hence the size of memory required depends on the resolution of the display. For instance, for a standard resolution of 80×25, the memory requirement may be calculated as follows:

Total number of characters per display = $80 \times 25 = 2000$

Since each character requires 2 bytes, then

Total size of memory = $2000 \times 2 = 4000$ bytes
= $4000/1024 = 3.906$KB or 4KB

Video pages

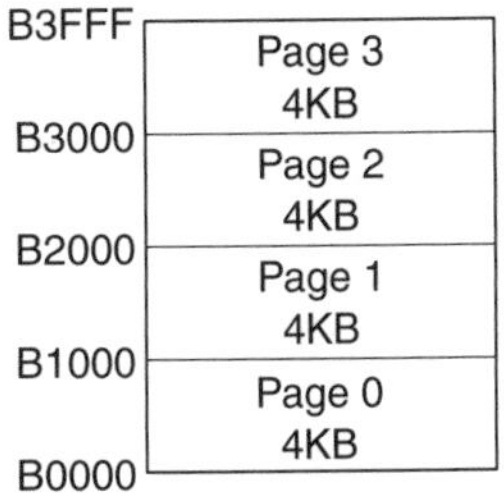

As can be seen from the above example, an 80×25 monochrome text display requires a video memory of only 4KB for one screen-full. This is one-eighth of the total video RAM allocated by DOS. The remaining memory space is made use of by storing additional screen-fulls known as video pages. In this case, eight such pages may be accommodated within the 32KB of monochrome video RAM. Fig. 14.21 shows four such video pages.

Only one page, the active page, will be displayed at any one time. Changes to the contents of the display may take place by changing the contents of an inactive page first, which is then switched with the active page for almost instant updating of the contents of the screen. Fast page switching allows a limited amount of animation. The PC may manage up to eight pages, each with its own defined cursor.

B3FFF	Page 3 4KB
B3000	Page 2 4KB
B2000	Page 1 4KB
B1000	Page 0 4KB
B0000	

Figure 14.21   Video paging

Graphic adaptor

In the graphic mode, display RAM locations already contain the monochrome/colour information of each pixel. There is no need for a character ROM or a character generator. They are thus disabled and the pixel video information is directly fed into the shift register.

In the graphic mode, the image is constructed by defining the intensity of each pixel, and in the case of colour, each triad dot individually. The video signal of a single line scan generated by the signal generator (Fig 14.19) is thus made up of a series of successive voltage levels representing the intensity of each pixel.

Memory requirements – graphic mode

The minimum bit requirement for a graphic display is 1 bit per pixel. A pixel can thus be bright (logic HIGH) or dark (logic LOW). For multi-colour (multi-shades for monochrome monitors) graphics, more than 1 bit is necessary to define the colour of each pixel. For example, if 2 bits are allocated, $2^2 = 4$ colours are made available. If the colour depth is increased to 3 bits, eight colours become available and so on. For 256 colours, 1 byte (8 bits) is necessary; 2 bytes (16 bits) per pixel provide 65,536 colours; and 'true' colour, with over 16 million colours, is obtained with 24 bits per pixel.

The size of video memory that is required depends on the resolution of the image as well as the number of colours that may be displayed. In general,

Video memory = resolution $\times$ bits per pixel/8 bytes

For example, a resolution of 320×200 with a 2-bit colour depth (four colours) requires a display memory of

$320 \times 200 \times 2 = 128,000$ bits or
$128,000/8 = 16,000$ bytes $= 16,000/1024 = 15.625$KB

This graphic mode will occupy part of the 128KB memory space

(A0000H to BFFFFH) made available by DOS architecture. The rest of the available memory space may be used for one or more video graphic pages.

An improved resolution and increased colour depth requires a larger display memory. For example, a 4-bit (16 colours), 640 × 340 resolution graphic display requires a video memory of

$$640 \times 340 \times 4 = 870,000 \text{ bits or}$$
$$870,000/8 = 108,000 \text{ bytes} = 108,000/1024 = 106.25\text{KB}$$

In practice, 128KB of memory will be made available, which is precisely the amount of memory space assigned by DOS. However, if the colour depth was doubled to 8 bits, the memory required would also double to 512KB which is larger than that made available by DOS's architecture. Table 14.3 lists standard graphic modes with their memory requirements.

Where the display RAM extends beyond the designated 128KB, it will overlap with the space allocated for expansion devices' ROM BIOS routines. To avoid this, the video memory on board the adaptor is divided into slices known as banks or pages of 64 or 128KB. Software is then used to allow the CPU to access each bank separately using the same 'paging' technique as that used for addressing expanded memory. This procedure inevitably introduces a delay in updating the displayed image. Modern video controllers move the entire display memory from real mode (A0000H to BFFFFH) to a protected mode memory space above the 1MB boundary. This linear mode of addressing the video memory eliminates paging and improves the performance of the adaptor.

Table 14.3 Video memory requirements

Resolution	Colour depth (bits)	No. of colours	Video memory	
			Bytes	Practical
640 × 480	4	16	153,600	256KB
	8	256	307,200	512KB
	16	65,536	614,400	1MB
	24	16,780,000	921,600	1MB
800 × 600	4	16	240,000	256KB
	8	256	480,000	512KB
	16	65,536	960,000	1MB
	24	16,780,000	1,440,000	2MB
1024 × 768	4	16	393,216	512KB
	8	256	786,432	1MB
	16	65,536	1,572,864	2MB
	24	16,780,000	2,359,296	4M
1280 × 1024	4	16	655,360	1MB
	8	256	1,310,720	2MB
	16	65,536	2,621,440	4MB
	24	16,780,000	3,932,160	4MB

Analogue adaptors TTL or digital monitors produce different colours (shades in the case of monochrome applications) by employing a number of signals which may be individually set to logic 1 (ON) or logic (OFF). Thus, a TTL monitor with three signals, red, green and blue, can produce $2^3 = 8$ different colours. This may be extended by introducing a fourth signal, intensity (I), resulting in $2^4 = 16$ colours. Further increases in colour depth require a larger number of signals, which makes the system unviable. For this reason, colour depths higher than 4 bits (16 colours) use analogue monitors which have the potential of displaying an infinite number of colours.

Before the video signal is sent to the analogue monitor, the digital coding used by the adaptor must be converted into an analogue signal using a digital-to-analogue converter (DAC). The DAC (Fig. 14.22) translates a multi-bit digital input into corresponding voltage levels. If this is repeated for successive digital inputs, an analogue waveform is constructed. The precision with which the output levels are produced is determined by the resolution of the DAC, i.e. the number of digital bits it can process. For instance, a 4-bit DAC is fed with a 4-bit input which may be converted into $2^4 = 16$ different voltage levels (Table 14.4) and a 6-bit DAC converts a 6-bit input

Table 14.4

Input code				Output level
B3	B2	B1	B0	
0	0	0	0	0.000
0	0	0	1	0.0625 × reference voltage
0	0	1	0	0.125 × reference voltage
0	0	1	1	0.187 × reference voltage
0	1	0	0	0.2500 × reference voltage
0	1	0	1	0.3125 × reference voltage
0	1	1	0	0.3750 × reference voltage
0	1	1	1	0.4375 × reference voltage
1	0	0	0	0.5000 × reference voltage
1	0	0	1	0.5625 × reference voltage
1	0	1	0	0.6250 × reference voltage
1	0	1	1	0.6875 × reference voltage
1	1	0	0	0.7500 × reference voltage
1	1	0	1	0.8125 × reference voltage
1	1	1	0	0.8750 × reference voltage
1	1	1	1	0.9375 × reference voltage

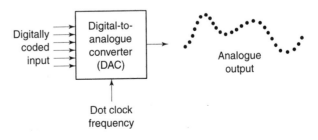

Figure 14.22 The analogue-to-digital converter (DAC)

into $2^6 = 64$ different levels and so on. The input is sampled at a rate determined by the dot frequency resulting in a voltage level being obtained for every pixel. The output is thus a series of voltage levels representing the strength of the video signal, pixel by pixel. This analogue output is fed into the cathode of the monitor to modulate the electron beam. In colour applications, three such signals are produced, R, G and B, using three different DACs which may be combined into a single chip.

Standard video modes   The development of PCs resulted in the introduction of a number of display modes which have become international standards. Each mode is given a number, usually in HEX, which defines the resolution of the display and consequently that of the monitor and the type of adaptor that must be used, such as MDA, EGA, VGA or SVGA. Table 14.5 lists some of the most common standard modes.

Table 14.5

Mode type HEX		IBM/ VESA	Resolution Graphic	Text	No. of colours	Adaptor type
HGC	Graphic	IBM	720 × 348		Mono	HGC
00/1	Text	IBM		40 × 25	16	HGC*, CGA, EGA, VGA
02/3	Text	IBM		80 × 25	16	HGC*, CGA, EGA, VGA
04/5	Graphic	IBM	320 × 200		4	HGC*, CGA, EGA, VGA
06	Graphic	IBM	640 × 200		2	HGC*, CGA, EGA, VGA
07	Text	IBM		80 × 25	Mono	MDA
0D/E	Graphic	IBM	320 × 200		16	EGA, VGA
0E	Graphic	IBM	640 × 200		16	EGA, VGA
0F	Graphic	IBM	640 × 350		Mono	EGA, VGA
10	Graphic	IBM	640 × 350		16	EGA, VGA
11	Graphic	IBM	640 × 480		2	VGA
12	Graphic	IBM	640 × 480		16	VGA
13	Graphic	IBM	320 × 200		256	VGA
100	Graphic	VESA	640 × 400		256	SVGA
100/1	Graphic	VESA	640 × 400		256	SVGA
102	Graphic	VESA	800 × 600		16	SVGA
103	Graphic	VESA	800 × 600		256	SVGA
104	Graphic	VESA	1024 × 768		16	SVGA
105	Graphic	VESA	1024 × 768		256	SVGA
106	Graphic	VESA	1280 × 1024		16	SVGA
107	Graphic	VESA	1280 × 1024		256	SVGA
108	Text	VESA		80 × 60		SVGA
109	Text	VESA		132 × 25		SVGA
10D	Graphic	VESA	320 × 200		32K	SVGA
111	Graphic	VESA	640 × 480		64K	SVGA
115	Graphic	VESA	800 × 600		16M	SVGA
116	Graphic	VESA	1024 × 768		32K	SVGA
11A	Graphic	VESA	1280 × 1024		64K	SVGA
11E	Graphic	VESA	1600 × 1200		16M	SVGA

* Hercules Graphic Card, HGC operates in monochrome only

Adaptor types Monochrome display adaptor (MDA)

The MDA is, as its name suggests, a black and white video display system introduced by IBM for the first XT computers. It is used in the text mode only with a resolution of 80×25.

Colour graphic adaptor (CGA)

The CGA was the first graphic-type adaptor from IBM which utilises TTL monitors. It has a maximum resolution of 640×200 pixels with two colours only. If the number of colours is increased to four, the resolution is halved to 320×200. In the text mode, it can be programmed to display 40×25 or 80×25 characters with 16 different colours.

Hercules graphic card (HGC)

The HGC is another monochrome adaptor. In the text mode, the HGC is the same as the MDA. However, unlike the MDA, it can operate in monochrome graphic mode with a resolution of 720×348.

Enhanced graphic adaptor (EGA)

The EGA provides a maximum resolution of 640×350 pixels with 16 different colours out of a 'palette' of 64 colours using TTL monitors. The arrangement of palettes is that shown in Fig. 14.23 in which the 4-bit colour code is used to select one of 16 6-bit registers known as palettes. Each register contains coded information which defines the colour of a pixel. Each time a pixel is scanned, one of the 16 registers is selected which then determines the colour of the pixel. The contents of the registers may be changed by the CPU thus altering the colour of the whole display. The CPU may set each palette register to one of $2^6 = 64$ different colours. In the EGA system, the 6 bits of the palette registers are used as digital signals to the monitor: red R, blue B, green G, red intensity RI, blue intensity BI and green intensity GI.

Since the PC's own system BIOS only supports MDA and CGA cards, EGA incorporates its own video ROM BIOS chip which is mounted on the card. With EGA, the size of the character matrix is not predefined by BIOS and may be changed by the user.

Video graphic array (VGA)

The video graphic array or adaptor (VGA) has a resolution of 640×350 pixels with 256 different colours (8-bit colour depth) out of a 'palette' of 256K colours. With such an enhanced colour capability,

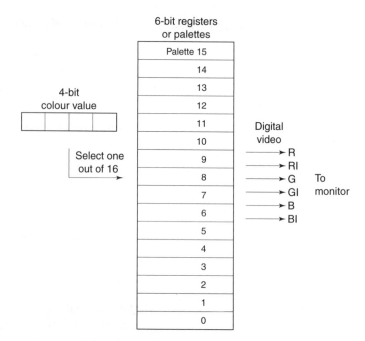

Figure 14.23 Palette arrangement for 16 × 64 = 256K colours

it is no longer possible to employ a digital monitor which, to produce that number of colours, will require 18 separate video lines. Instead, an analogue monitor is used. A digital-to-analogue converter (DAC) is therefore needed to convert digitally coded signals into analogue values. Three DACs are used, one for each primary colour. A single integrated palette DAC, also known as RAMDAC, is used which incorporates the palette registers as well as the three converters. The basic principles of VGA colour generation are illustrated in Fig. 14.24. The RAMDAC contains 256 × 18-bit registers. Each register is divided into three groups of 6 bits each. Each 6-bit group defines the intensity of a primary colour, the first for red, the second for green and the third for blue. Three separate DACs are used to convert the 6-bit digitally coded intensity into an analogue value which is fed into the appropriate gun of the colour tube. The 6-bit converters can produce $2^6 = 64$ different values for each primary colour. Since the colour on the screen is a result of adding the three primary colours, then the total number of different colours that may be obtained by each palette is

$$64^3 = 262,144 = 256K$$

(The same figure may be arrived at by $2^{18} = 262,144$.) The number of colours that may be displayed simultaneously is determined by the number of registers or palettes, i.e. 256 colours. For each pixel, a palette is selected by selecting one of the 256 registers by the setting of an 8-bit colour value.

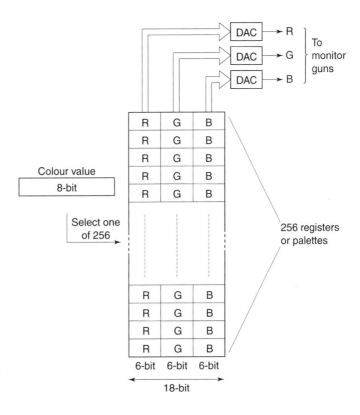

Figure 14.24   Palette arrangement for
$256 \times 256 = 16$ million colours

Super VGA (SVGA)

The SVGA was established as a standard with the introduction of the
VESA (Video Electronic Standards Association) bus. A BIOS
extension was introduced and is used as an interface between the
programmer and the adaptor. SVGA is capable of a resolution of up
to 1600×1200 and 24-bit colour depth (16,777,216 colours).

Video connectors   Fig. 14.25 shows the connectors used for each type of video adaptor.
The 15-pin VGA/SVGA connector has 3 identification (ID) pins:
ID0 (pin 11), ID1 (pin 12) and ID2 (pin 4). The pins are either
earthed (OV) or left open circuit (NC) to inform the PC of the type
of monitor used (Table 14.6).

Table 14.6

Monitor type	Pin 12	Pin 11	Pin 4
Mono	NC	OV	NC
Non-interlaced colour	OV	NC	NC
Interlaced colour	OV	NC	OV

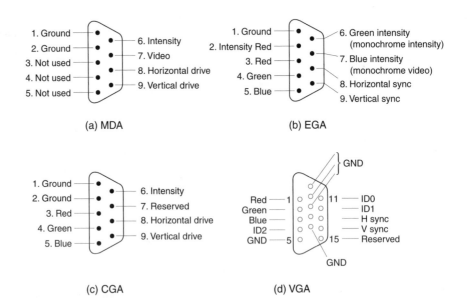

Figure 14.25 Video connectors and their pin-out

Improving video speed

Updating, i.e. changing the contents of a displayed image, involves changing the contents of the video RAM. The rate at which an image can be updated is thus determined by the speed with which data can be written to video RAM. This involves the processor moving data across the expansion bus and into the video memory chips on the video adaptor. The amount of data that has to be entered into video RAM for a complete update, i.e. a complete change of screen contents, is dependent on the resolution of the display and its colour depth. For example, a single image of 640×480 pixels and 8-bit colour depth requires

$$640 \times 480 \times 8/8 = 307{,}200 \text{ bytes}$$

If the image is to be updated 10 times per second, then the data throughput is

$$307{,}200 \times 10 = 3{,}072{,}000 \text{ bytes/s}$$

Higher throughputs are required for improved resolution and increased colour capabilities.

The speed with which such throughput of data can be moved is determined by three factors: the speed of video RAM, the speed with which data may be moved across the expansion bus and the processing speed.

The speed of video RAM may be improved by using dual-port VRAM chips. The speed of data transfer across the expansion bus may be improved by the use of a local bus such as the VESA local bus or the PCI bus. The processing speed may be improved by using a faster processor. However, a very fast processor is still constrained by the limited throughput of the expansion bus. The processing speed may be improved by incorporating a separate coprocessor or accelerator on the video adaptor.

Video accelerators   A video accelerator is a special purpose processor which relieves the CPU of some of the time-consuming video processing. In its basic form, it can carry out a number of functions when instructed to do so by the system processor. Such tasks include line draw, square fill and BitBLT (Bit Boundary bLock Transfer). BitBLT is a graphic drawing routine which moves a rectangle of data from one area of the screen to another. In all such cases, the CPU only needs to transfer the start and end positions of the graphic line or block and its colour value. The accelerator then draws the graphics itself. Higher performance graphic adaptors will employ graphic processors which can carry out complex graphic instructions and process complete programs.

15 The keyboard and the mouse

The essential elements of a keyboard are a switch matrix and a keyboard interface encoder chip (Fig. 15.1). The keyboard encoder is a customised microprocessor with an in-built ROM such as the 8048 or the more recent 8049 or compatibles like the Motorola 6805. The switch matrix consists of a number of horizontal and vertical lines crossing each other. At each crossing, a small switch operated by a spring-loaded key is located. When a key is pressed, the switch closes and the relevant horizontal and vertical lines are shorted. This is then detected by the keyboard encoder which generates a special 8-bit code known as the scan code. Each key is allocated its own unique scan code defined by the first 7 bits, b0 to b6, as shown in Fig. 15.2. The eighth bit, b7, is used to distinguish between a key-make (b7 = 0) and a key-release (b7 = 1). The scan code is entered into an internal buffer for transmission to the computer via a special serial cable.

Mechanical switches suffer from what is known as contact bounce caused by the spring action of the switch which results in several contacts being made before coming to rest. Spikes are generated which may be interpreted as multiple keystrokes. To prevent this, a low pass filter is incorporated with a time constant ensuring that intentional double strokes pass through unaffected.

On the computer side, a keyboard controller, also known as the keyboard BIOS chip, receives the serial data stream and converts it into an appropriate ASCII code. The keyboard controller is another dedicated processor such as the 8042 or the more modern 8741/8742 with an in-built few kilobytes of ROM and few hundred bytes of RAM.

Data transfer

Data transfer between the keyboard and the computer is carried out synchronously using two communication lines: data and clock

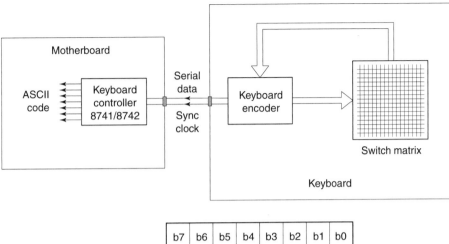

Figure 15.1 The keyboard interface

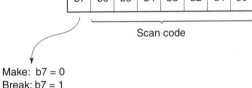

Scan code

Make: b7 = 0
Break: b7 = 1

Figure 15.2 The keyboard scan code

together with ground line. The data line carries serial data units (SDUs) consisting of an 11-bit package. The package is divided into a start bit, eight data bits, a parity bit and a stop bit. When a key is pressed, the keyboard encoder sends the scan code associated with the selected key with bit 7 at logic 0. This is known as the make-code. When the key is released, the same scan code is generated, but this time with bit 7 set to logic 1. When the keyboard controller on the motherboard receives the make-code, it interrupts the operation of the processor by enabling IRQ1. The CPU responds by calling a keyboard driver routine which, using an internal conversion table, converts the scan code into an ASCII code. When the key is released, the keyboard encoder sends a break-code to the keyboard controller which terminates the action.

A number of conversion tables are available which may be individually selected by loading the COUNTRY.SYS routine as a device driver in CONFIG.SYS.

Types of keyboards

The original 83-key XT keyboard is a unidirectional device which could not be programmed by the computer. Two-way communication was introduced with the 84-key AT keyboard which was then followed by the enhanced 101-key or 102-key multi-function MFII keyboard. The enhanced keyboard has a separate numeric keypad, separate cursor control keys and a set of 12 function keys. The enhanced keyboard is fully programmable by computer software for different layouts to suit different languages.

Keyboard and display configuration

Keyboard configuration involves determining a character set together with country-specific conventions and setting the character layout on the keyboard.

Different character sets are contained in the DISPLAY.SYS file which must be loaded in CONFIG.SYS as a device driver. A typical command is

DEVICE=C:\DOS\DISPLAY.SYS

Country-specific conventions are included in COUNTRY.SYS which must be loaded in CONFIG.SYS. A typical command line for English (UK) is

COUNTRY=044,,C:\DOS\COUNTRY.SYS

A different configuration may be produced by using the appropriate international telephone country code in place of 044, e.g. 033 for France and 039 for Italy. The default code is English (USA).

Different layouts are available in the MS-DOS KEYB command which may be entered at the prompt or in AUTOEXEC.BAT. A typical command line for English (UK) is

KEYB UK,,C:\DOS\KEYBOARD.SYS

Other configurations may be obtained by using the appropriate country code in place of UK, such as US for English (USA), IT for Italian and FR for French. A full list is provided by DOS's HELP.

Keyboard interface connector

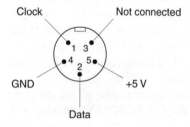

Figure 15.3 Keyboard connector pin-out

On the computer side, a 5-pin DIN socket is made available for the keyboard serial cable (Fig. 15.3). One line, pin 2, is used for serial data, and a second line, pin 1, is used for the synchronising clock. The keyboard receives its 5 V d.c. power from the motherboard on pin 5 with pin 4 used for signal ground.

The mouse

The mouse or track ball is a relatively new input device for a computer gaining its popularity with the introduction of the graphical user interface (GUI) such as in Windows. The function of a mouse is to convert a small movement of the mouse into digital signals which may be interpreted into corresponding movement of a pointer on the screen. The digital signals may be produced by the rotary movement of a variable resistor in the mechanical type of

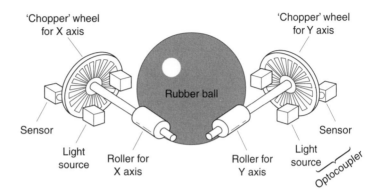

Figure 15.4 Main components of an optical mouse

mouse or the interruption of a light beam by a rotating wheel in the opto-mechanical type. Mice may have one, two or three control buttons which operate corresponding microswitches.

The basic components of an optical mouse are shown in Fig. 15.4. The rubber ball rests against two rollers, X and Y, placed to detect the horizontal and vertical movements of the ball. The two rollers are connected to two small wheels or disks with a fine grill. Each wheel is placed in the light path of two opto-couplers. The opto-couplers detect the movement of the wheel and produce a stream of pulses as the light beam is interrupted by the grill. These pulses are fed into the mouse interface chip which converts them to a coded serial signal for transmission to the computer. Each wheel and its associated opto-couplers are designed in such a way as to be able to detect the direction of the movement of each roller, left/right for X and up/down for Y, producing positive pulses for one direction (left for X and up for Y) and negative pulses for the other direction (right for X and down for Y).

A third and more reliable type of mouse is a purely optical device which contains no moving parts. Instead of the chopped wheel/opto-coupler combination, an LED/phototransistor sensor device is used to detect movement on a special mat marked with a fine grid. As the mouse moves across the grid, the sensor sends pulses to the mouse interface which are processed in the same way as those produced by the opto-mechanical mouse.

Mouse interface

There are three methods by which a mouse may interface with a computer: serial, dedicated motherboard and bus card.

In the serial type, the mouse is connected to one of the available serial ports, normally COM1 or COM2. The device driver will, during the initialisation stage, search and determine which COM port the mouse is using.

The motherboard mouse uses a dedicated port built into the motherboard. This was introduced by IBM with the PS/2 system and hence it is also known as the PS/2 mouse interface. While this type of interface releases one of the COM ports, it none the less has to be assigned an IRQ, normally IRQ12, and an I/O port address, normally 60H or 64H.

In cases where neither a serial port nor a motherboard interface is available, a bus mouse may be used. In this case, a mouse adaptor card is used which is slotted into an 8-bit ISA expansion bus. The disadvantage of this type of mouse interface is the fact that a valuable expansion slot is occupied.

Software requirements

Signals from the mouse interface chip are translated into a movement of the pointer by a device driver which is either separately loaded or part of the system's software. Loading a mouse driver may be carried out by including MOUSE.SYS (or IMOUSE.SYS or GRMOUSE.SYS etc. as provided by the manufacturer's software) as a device driver in CONFIG.SYS or calling the MOUSE.COM (or IMOUSE.COM etc.) routine in AUTOEXEC.BAT. Mouse manufacturers usually provide an INSTALL routine which carries out the mouse installation automatically.

A typical device driver line in CONFIG.SYS is

DEVICE = C:\MOUSE\MOUSE.SYS

A typical command line in AUTOEXEC.BAT is

C:\MOUSE\MOUSE.COM

16 Motherboard configuration and installation

Motherboards are identified by the processor, the size and type of system and cache memories, the type and number of expansion slots they offer, as well as any other peripheral functions provided by on-board ICs such as disk drive and video display controllers. Typical specifications which are provided by the motherboard manufacturer are shown in Table 16.1.

Typical layouts Fig. 16.1 illustrates the layout of a basic 486 motherboard supporting four 30-pin and two 72-pin SIMM slots, four 16-bit ISA and three PCI expansion slots, together with one VESA extension and L2 cache memory module slot.

A Pentium motherboard is illustrated in Fig. 16.2. This motherboard supports 256 or 512KB secondary (L2) cache, four ISA and four PCI expansion slots, three banks comprising two 72-pin SIMM slots each, two built-in enhanced IDE and floppy disk adaptors, two fast UART 16550A serial ports, an enhanced parallel port and a mouse interface.

Table 16.1 Typical motherboard specifications

486SX, DX, DX2 or DX4 microprocessor, with external CPU bus speeds of 25 or 33 MHz

Option for Intel Pentium OverDrive^{TM} processor

System RAM up to 64MB

Optional 256KB cache memory module

Local bus IDE hard drive connector (primary IDE channel), supporting up to two IDE drives (hard drives suggested)

AT bus IDE hard drive connector (secondary IDE channel), supporting up to two IDE drives (CD-ROM drive suggested)

VGA subsystem with extended resolutions supported by 1MB or 2MB of video DRAM

Three or five usable expansion slots, comprising two or three each PC AT-bus and PCI local bus slots, with one shared slot

Connector for floppy drives

I/O ports: two serial and one parallel

PS/2-compatible keyboard and mouse connectors

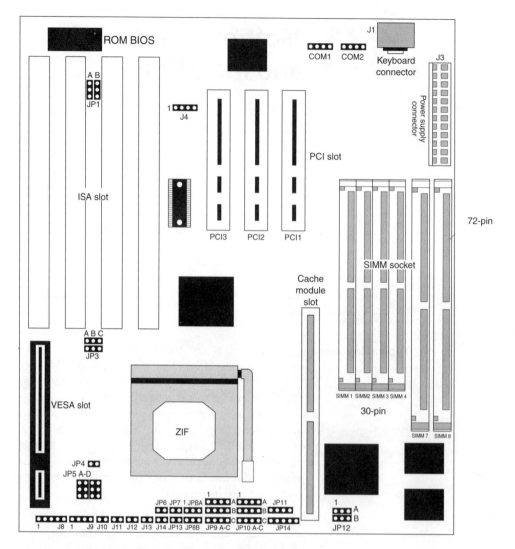

Figure 16.1 A basic 80486 motherboard layout

Configuration

Before a new motherboard is used, it must first be configured and installed. Configuration may also have to be carried out when a motherboard is upgraded with a more powerful processor.

The purpose of configuration is to set the operational features of the motherboard as determined by, among other things, the type of the processor and size of cache memory. Configuration is carried out by setting a number of jumpers. The number and functions of these jumper vary from one motherboard to the next. A simple 386SX motherboard has a few jumpers and configuration is easy, whilst a

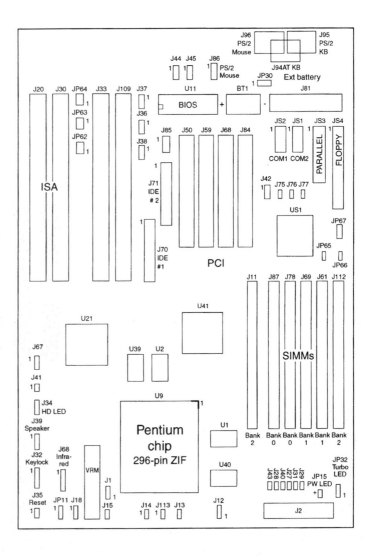

Figure 16.2 Pentium motherboard layout

modern Pentium motherboard contains more numerous and more complex jumper settings. The function and options of all jumper settings are provided in the manufacturer's user manual or printed on the board itself or both. A typical motherboard layout showing jumper settings and pin assignments is illustrated in Fig. 16.3.

Jumper settings may be divided into the following configuration groups:

CPU-specific. This is the largest group of jumpers which configure the motherboard for the selected processor. They include a set of jumpers for the particular make of CPU, CPU speed, CPU internal clock and CPU working voltage (5 V or 3.3/ 3.45 V). Universal motherboards (UMBs) use auto-detect to set the correct working voltage of the CPU. Some motherboards employ a subassembly for setting the correct working voltage for

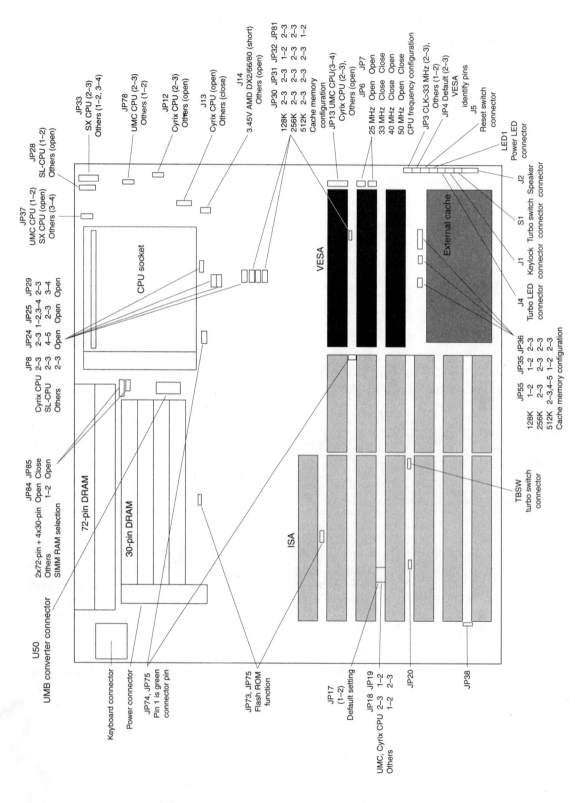

Figure 16.3 Motherboard layout with jumper settings

Table 16.2 CPU jumper settings

CPU	JP8	JP12	JP13	JP18	JP19	JP24	JP25	JP28	JP29	JP33	JP37	JP40	J11	J13	J14	JP78
486SX	2–3	Open	Open	1–2	2–3	Open	Open	Open	Open	2–3	Open	2–3	Open	Close	Open	1–2
3.45 V AMD 486 DX2/66/80	2–3	Open	Open	1–2	2–3	Open	Open	Open	Open	1–2 3–4	3–4	2–3	Open	Close	Close	1–2
486DX	2–3	Open	Open	1–2	2–3	Open	Open	Open	Open	1–2 3–4	3–4	2–3	Open	Close	Open	1–2
AMD40	2–3	Open	Open	1–2	2–3	Open	Open	Open	Open	1–2 3–4	3–4	2–3	Open	Close	Open	1–2
SL-486SX	2–3	Open	Open	1–2	2–3	4–5	2–3	1–2	3–4	2–3	Open	2–3	Open	Close	Open	1–2
SL-486DX	2–3	Open	Open	1–2	2–3	4–5	2–3	1–2	3–4	1–2 3–4	3–4	2–3	Open	Close	Open	1–2
SL-486DX2	2–3	Open	Open	1–2	2–3	4–5	2–3	1–2	3–4	1–2 3–4	3–4	2–3	Open	Close	Open	1–2
Intel 486DX4-100	2–3	Open	Open	1–2	2–3	4–5	2–3	1–2	3–4	1–2 3–4	3–4	2–3	Open	Close	Open	1–2
AMD DX4-100	2–3	Open	Open	1–2	2–3	Open	Open	Open	Open	1–2 3–4	3–4	2–3	Open	Close	Open	1–2
Cyrix 486DX	2–3	2–3	2–3	2–3	1–2	2–3	1–2 3–4	Open	2–3	1–2 3–4	3–4	2–3	Open	Open	Open	1–2
UMC 486SX	2–3	Open	3–4	2–3	1–2	Open	Open	Open	Open	2–3	1–2	2–3	Open	Close	Open	2–3
AMD Enhanced DX4	1–2	1–2	Open	1–2	1–2	4–5	2–3	2–3	1–2 3–4	1–2 3–4	2–3	2–3	Close	Close	Open	1–2

Note: For AMD486DX-40 Version C CPU, JP40 (1–2) is shorted.
For all DX4–100 CPU, set JP10 (open).

Table 16.3 CPU frequency settings

CPU	25 MHz	33 MHz	40 MHz	50 MHz
JP6	Open	Close	Close	Open
JP7	Open	Close	Open	Close

Table 16.4 CPU multiplier

JP44	CPU internal clock option
1–2	X2
Open	X3

Table 16.5 Cache memory settings

Cache size	Cache RAM	Tag RAM	JP30	JP31	JP32	JP35	JP36	JP81	JP55
128 KB	32 KB×8 U (31–34)	8 KB×8 U 26	2–3	2–3	1–2	1–2	2–3	2–3	1–2
256 KB	32 KB×8 U (27–34)	32 KB×8 U 26	2–3	2–3	2–3	2–3	2–3	2–3	2–3
256 KB	64 KB×8 U (31–34)	32 KB×8 U 26	2–3	2–3	2–3	1–2	2–3	2–3	1–2, 3–4
512 KB	128 KB×8 U (31–34)	32 KB×8 U 26	2–3	2–3	2–3	1–2	2–3	1–2	1–2, 3–4, 5–6
512 KB	64 KB×8 U (27–34)	32 KB×8 U 26	2–3	2–3	2–3	2–3	2–3	1–2	2–3, 4–5
1 MB	128 KB×8 U (27–34)	64 KB×8 U 26	2–3	2–3	2–3	2–3	2–3	1–2	2–3, 4–5, 6–7

the processor. Tables 16.2, 16.3 and 16.4 show the CPU-specific jumper setting options for the motherboard in Fig. 16.3.

Clock speed. Where the speed of the CPU is greater than 33 MHz, a jumper must be set which introduces the necessary wait states for the expansion slots.

Cache memory configuration. Motherboards provide a number of IC socket holders or module slots for secondary cache memory. These must be filled and jumper settings configured in accordance with the manufacturer's specifications. A typical set of cache configurations is listed in Table 16.5.

Quick configuration test

If the power cable and the loudspeaker are now connected then an initial test may be carried out. This involves turning the power on and listening to any audible beeps. One or more beeps indicate that the clock is functioning and that the CPU speed configuration is correct. If no beeps are produced, the clock speed and CPU multiplier should be checked.

Installation   Installation involves installing system memory, connecting power and other adaptor cables, connecting the indicators (loudspeaker and LEDs) and other facilities that are made available by the motherboard, and finally configuring CMOS BIOS set-up.

Memory installation

Motherboards provide a number of memory banks utilising either 30-pin or 72-pin SIMMs, or both. These slots must be filled in accordance with the manufacturer's recommendations. Where both types of SIMMs are used, system RAM configuration jumpers may have to be set, such as the SIMM RAM selection jumpers J84 and J85 in Fig. 16.3. Typical system memory configuration options for the motherboard in Fig. 16.3 are listed in Table 16.6.

Table 16.6 SIMMs configuration

(a) 72-pin SIMM RAM only

Option	X SIMM 1	X SIMM 2	Total memory
1	1MB-S	1MB-S	2MB
2	2MB-D	2MB-D	4MB
3	4MB-S	4MB-S	8MB
4	4MB-S	8MB-D	12MB
5	8MB-D	8MB-D	16MB
6	8MB-D	16MB-S	24MB
7	16MB-S	16MB-S	32MB
8	32MB-D	32MB-D	64MB

(b) 30-pin SIMM RAM only

Option	SIMM 1 to SIMM 4	Total memory
1	256KB	1MB
2	1MB	4MB
3	4MB	16MB
4	16MB	64MB (not tested)

(c) one 72-pin and 30-pin SIMM RAMs

Option	X SIMM 2	X SIMM 1 to 4	Total memory
1	4MB	1MB	8MB
2	16MB	1MB	20MB
3	16MB	4MB	32MB

(d) two 72-pin and 30-pin SIMM RAMs

Option	X SIMM 1 to 4	X SIMM 1 to 2	Total memory
1	1MB	1MB-S	6MB
2	1MB	2MB-D	8MB
3	1MB	4MB-S	12MB
4	4MB	4MB-S	24MB
5	4MB	16MB-S	48MB

Installing connector cables

Typically, motherboards provide a number of standard connectors such as power, keyboard, keylock, loudspeaker, turbo switch, turbo LED and reset. Connectors are also provided for on-board functions such as hard disk and floppy drive interfaces, serial and parallel ports, CD-ROM and video adaptor. In installing connector cables, care must be taken to ensure the correct orientation. Except where orientation is not relevant, plugs are keyed for correct insertion or pin 1 is identified on the motherboard.

Configuring CMOS set-up

Once the motherboard has been configured and the memory and all available adaptors installed, the computer may be turned on. The booting-up process begins with the BIOS routines taking over. Following the memory test, which if successful will result in a single audible beep, BIOS displays a message on the screen which provides an opportunity to enter CMOS (or BIOS) set-up. CMOS set-up is a menu-driven process which allows the user to specify the type of hardware installation, such as disk drives, select optional features such as system boot-up sequence and set functional properties such as the number of wait states.

CMOS set-up is divided into three basic groupings: standard, advanced and chipset. Both the advanced and the chipset set-up vary with the BIOS and the actual chipset used in the motherboard and should not be casually varied. As a safety precaution, BIOS manufacturers provide a return to factory settings facility.

The standard set-up allows the user to set the time, date, and the number and type of floppy and hard disk drives installed. The user may choose one (floppy A:) or two (floppies A: and B:) drives as well as one master hard disk or two (master and slave) hard disks. For the floppy disk drives, all possible options (5¼ and 3½ inch, double density and high density) are available. For the hard disk, a table listing the parameters of 46 standard types is provided, one of which may be selected (Table 16.7). A further type 47 is provided which may be used to set the parameters of a hard disk that is not included in the standard table. The auto-detect facility is normally available which can detect the drive type listing its parameters. Otherwise, they have to be entered manually using the information provided by the hard disk manufacturer.

The advanced set-up allows the user to determine a number of operational features of the system. A typical list of options offered by the advanced set-up is shown in Table 16.8. Some of the options are entirely a matter of user preference such as typematic rate and boot-up sequence. Others such as Pri-master LBA mode are determined by the type of hardware, in this case the primary or master hard disk, installed.

The chipset set-up configures more advanced operating properties of the system. A typical list of options is illustrated in Table 16.9.

Table 16.7   Hard disk drive table

Type	Cylinders	Heads	Write precomp.	LZ	Sector	Size (MB)
1	306	4	128	305	17	10
2	615	4	300	615	17	20
3	615	6	300	615	17	31
4	940	8	512	940	17	62
5	940	6	512	940	17	47
6	615	4	65,535	615	17	20
7	462	8	256	511	17	31
8	733	5	65,535	733	17	30
9	900	15	65,535	901	17	112
10	820	3	65,535	820	17	20
11	855	5	65,535	855	17	35
12	855	7	65,535	855	17	50
13	306	8	128	319	17	20
14	733	7	65,535	733	17	43
15	–	–	–	–	–	–
16	612	4	0	663	17	20
17	977	5	300	977	17	41
18	977	7	65,535	977	17	57
19	1024	7	512	1023	17	60
20	733	5	300	732	17	30
21	733	7	300	732	17	43
22	733	5	300	733	17	30
23	306	4	0	336	17	10
24	925	7	0	925	17	54
25	925	9	65,535	925	17	69
26	754	7	754	754	17	44
27	754	11	65,535	754	17	69
28	699	7	256	699	17	41
29	823	10	65,535	823	17	68
30	918	7	918	918	17	53
31	1024	11	65,535	1024	17	94
32	1024	15	65,535	1024	17	128
33	1024	5	1024	1024	17	43
34	612	2	128	612	17	10
35	1024	9	65,535	1024	17	77
36	1024	8	512	1024	17	68
37	615	8	128	615	17	41
38	987	3	987	987	17	25
39	987	7	987	987	17	57
40	820	6	820	820	17	41
41	977	5	977	977	17	41
42	981	5	981	981	17	41
43	830	7	512	830	17	48
44	830	10	65,535	830	17	69
45	917	15	65,535	918	17	114
46	1224	15	65,535	1223	17	152
47	User					

Table 16.8 Advanced set-up

Typematic Rate (Chars/Sec)	Typematic rate sets the rate at which characters on the screen repeat when a key is pressed and held down. The settings are *15, 20* or *30* characters per second
System Keyboard	This option does not specify if a keyboard is attached to the computer. Rather, it specifies if error messages are displayed if a keyboard is not attached. This option permits you to configure workstations with no keyboards. The settings are *Absent* or *Present*
Primary Display	Select this option to configure the type of monitor attached to the computer. The settings are *Mono, CGA 80x25, Color 40x25, VGA/EGA,* or *Absent*
Mouse Support	When this option is enabled, WinBIOS supports a PS/2-type mouse. The settings are *Enabled* or *Disabled*
Above 1MB Memory Test	When this option is enabled, the WinBIOS memory test is performed on all system memory. When this option is disabled, the memory test is done only on the first 1MB of system memory. The settings are *Enabled* or *Disabled*
Memory Test Tick Sound	This option enables (turns on) or disables (turns off) the ticking sound during the memory test. The settings are *Enabled* or *Disabled*
Parity Error Check	This option enables or disables parity error checking for system RAM. The settings are *Enabled* (all system RAM parity is checked) or *Disabled* (parity is checked only on the first 1MB of system RAM)
Hit DEL Message Display	Disabling this option prevents – *Hit <DEL> if you want to run Setup* – from appearing when the system boots. The settings are *Enabled* or *Disabled*
Extended BIOS RAM Area	Specify in this option if the top 1KB of the system programming area beginning at 639K or 0:300 in the system BIOS area in low memory will be used to store hard disk information. The settings are *Top 1K* or *0:300*
Wait for <F1> If Any Error	WinBIOS POST runs system diagnostic tests that can generate a message followed by – *Press <F1> to continue* – If this option is enabled, Win BIOS waits for the end user to press <F1> before continuing. If this option is disabled, WinBIOS continues the boot process without waiting for <F1> to be pressed. The settings are *Enabled* or *Disabled*
System Boot-up Num Lock	When *On*, this option turns on/off *Num Lock* when the system is powered. The settings are *On* or *Off*
Floppy Drive Seek At Boot	When this option is enabled, WinBIOS performs a SEEK command on floppy drive A: before booting the system. The settings are *Enabled* or *Disabled*
System Boot-up Sequence	This option sets the sequence of boot drives (either floppy drive A: or hard disk drive C:)that WinBIOS attempts to boot from after POST completes. The settings are *C:,A:* or *A:,C:*.
System Boot-up CPU Speed	This option specifies the speed of the CPU at system boot time. The settings are *High* or *Low*
External Cache	This option enables (turns on) or disables (turns off) the secondary cache memory. The settings are *Disabled, Enabled*
Internal Cache	This option enables (turns on) or disables (turns off) the CPU built-in cache memory. The settings are *Disabled, Enabled*
Turbo Switch Function	When this option is set to *Enabled,* the externally mounted turbo switch is enabled. The settings are *Enabled* or *Disabled*
Password Checking	This option enables the password check option every time the system boots or the end user runs Setup. If *Always* is chosen, a user password prompt appears every time the computer is turned on. If *Setup* is chosen, the password prompt appears if AMI WinBIOS Setup is executed
Video Shadow C000, 16K	When this option is set to *Enabled*, the video ROM area from C0000H to C3FFFH is copied (shadowed) to RAM for faster execution
Video Shadow C400, 16K	When this option is set to *Enabled*, the video ROM area from C4000H to C7FFFH is copied (shadowed) to RAM for faster execution
Shadow C800, 16K	This option enables (turns on) or disables (turns off) the shadowing function of the contents of ROM area named in the option title. The settings are *Disabled, Enabled*

Table 16.8 (Continued)

Shadow CC00, 16K	This option enables (turns on) or disables (turns off) the shadowing function of the contents of ROM area named in the option title. The settings are *Disabled, Enabled*
Shadow D000, 16K	This option enables (turns on) or disables (turns off) the shadowing function of the contents of ROM area named in the option title. The settings are *Disabled, Enabled*
Shadow D400, 16K	This option enables (turns on) or disables (turns off) the shadowing function of the contents of ROM area named in the option title. The settings are *Disabled, Enabled*
Shadow D800, 16K	This option enables (turns on) or disables (turns off) the shadowing function of the contents of ROM area named in the option title. The settings are *Disabled, Enabled*
Shadow DC00, 16K	This option enables (turns on) or disables (turns off) the shadowing function of the contents of ROM area named in the option title. The settings are *Disabled, Enabled*
Shadow E000, 32K	This option enables (turns on) or disables (turns off) the shadowing function of the contents of ROM area named in the option title. The settings are *Disabled, Enabled*
Main BIOS Shadow F000, 64K	This option enables (turns on) or disables (turns off) the shadowing function of the contents of ROM area named in the option title. The settings are *Disabled, Enabled*
IDE Block Mode	This option enables (turns on) or disables (turns off) the block mode data transfer of the IDE hard disks. The settings are *Auto, 2, 4,* or *8*
Pri-Master 32-Bit Transfer	This option enables (turns on) or disables (turns off) the 32-bit transfer function for the primary master IDE hard disk. The settings are *Disabled, Enabled*
Pri-Master Block MODE	This option enables (turns on) or disables (turns off) the block mode for the primary master IDE hard disk. The settings are *Disabled, Enabled*
Pri-Master LBA MODE	This option enables (turns on) or disables (turns off) the logical block addressing for the primary master IDE hard disk. The settings are *Disabled, Enabled*. If the IDE hard disk capacity is greater 528MB, this option should be enabled
Pri-Slave 32-Bit Transfer	This option enables (turns on) or disables (turns off) the 32-bit transfer function for the primary slave IDE hard disk. The settings are *Disabled, Enabled*
Pri-Slave Block MODE	This option enables (turns on) or disables (turns off) the block mode for the primary slave IDE hard disks. The settings are *Disabled, Enabled*
Pri-Slave LBA MODE	This option enables (turns on) or disables (turns off) the logical block addressing for the primary slave IDE hard disk. The settings are *Disabled, Enabled*. If the IDE hard disk capacity is greater than 528MB, this option should be enabled
Secondary Master Present	This option specifies whether the secondary master hard disk is present. The settings are *Disabled, Enabled*
Sec-Master 32-Bit Transfer	This option enables (turns on) or disables (turns off) the 32-bit transfer function for the secondary master IDE hard disk. The settings are *Disabled, Enabled*
Sec-Master Block MODE	This option enables (turns on) or disables (turns off) the block mode for the secondary master IDE hard disk. The settings are *Disabled, Enabled*
Sec-Master LBA MODE	This option enables (turns on) or disables (turns off) the logical block addressing for the secondary master IDE hard disk. The settings are *Disabled, Enabled*. If the IDE hard disk capacity is greater than 528MB, this option should be enabled
Secondary Slave Present	This option specifies whether the secondary slave hard disk is present. The settings are *Disabled, Enabled*
Sec-Slave 32-Bit Transfer	This option enables (turns on) or disables (turns off) the 32-bit transfer function for the secondary slave IDE hard disk. The settings are *Disabled, Enabled*
Sec-Slave Block MODE	This option enables (turns on) or disables (turns off) the block mode for the secondary slave IDE hard disk. The settings are *Disabled, Enabled*
Sec-Slave LBA MODE	This option enables (turns on) or disables (turns off) the logical block addressing for the secondary slave IDE hard disk. The settings are *Disabled, Enabled*. If the IDE hard disk capacity is greater than 528MB, this option should be enabled

Table 16.9 Chipset set-up

AUTO config function	The settings of this option are *Enable/Disabled*. If it is enabled, the BIOS will automatically set up the 'Cache Read Hit Wait State', 'Cache Write Hit Wait State', 'DRAM Wait State Select', 'DRAM Page Mode', 'Keyboard Clock Select', 'AT Clock Select', options in the chipset set-up. When it is disabled, users can set these options to their own choice.
Cache Read Hit Wait State	This option specifies the number of wait state when cache read hit. The settings are *3-2-2, 3-1-1-1*, or *2-1-1-1*
Cache Write Hit Wait State	This option specifies the number of wait state when cache write hit. The settings are *2 W.S., 1 W.S.*, or *0 W.S*
DRAM Wait State Select	This option specifies the number of wait state of DRAM. The settings are *2 W.S., 1 W.S.*, or *0 W.S*
DRAM Page Mode	This option specifies the DRAM supported page mode method. The settings are *Normal* or *Fast*
Keyboard Clock Select	This option specifies the clock speed of the keyboard controller. The settings are *PCLK/6, PCLK/5, PCLK/4, PCLK/3, PCLK/2, 9.5 MHz*, or *7.2 MHz*
AT Clock Select	This option specifies the clock speed of the AT BUS I/O. The settings are *PCLK/6, PCLK/5, PCLK/4, PCLK/3, PCLK/2* or *PCLK/8*
Alt Bit in Tag SRAM	This option specifies the location of the Alt bit and the Tag bit. The settings are *8+0 bits* or *7+1 bits*. *7+1* means both the Alt and Tag bits are located in the same SRAM. *8+0* means the Alt bit is located in another SRAM
Local Ready Delay Setting	This option specifies the delay time of the local ready signal. The settings are *No Delay, Delay lT, Delay 2T*, or *Delay 3T*
Signal LDEV# Sample Time	This option specifies the sampling time of the LDEV# signal. The settings are *in T2, in T3, in T4*, or *in T5*
CPU ADS# Delay 1T or Not	This option specifies the delay time of the CPU ADS# signal. The settings are *No Delay* or *Delay lT*
Hardware DRAM Parity Check	This option enables (turns on) or disables (turns off) the hardware DRAM parity check function. The settings are *Disabled* or *Enabled*
ISA Bus Refresh Disable Bit	This option specifies the ISA bus refresh cycle. The settings are *Slow* or *Fast*
DRAM Refresh Method	This option specifies the refresh method of the DRAM. The settings are *RAS only* or *CAS/RAS*
Divider for Refresh	This option specifies the system refresh. The settings are *1/64, 1/1, 1/2, 1/4, 1/8, 1/16*, or *1/32*
System Memory Remap or Not	This option enables (turns on) or disables (turns off) the system memory remap function. The settings are *Disabled* or *Enabled*
Video ROM Cache C000, 16K	This option enables (turns on) or disables (turns off) the caching function of the contents of ROM area named in the option title. The settings are *Disabled* or *Enabled*
Video ROM Cache C400, 16K	This option enables (turns on) or disables (turns off) the caching function of the contents of ROM area named in the option title. The settings are *Disabled* or *Enabled*
Adaptor ROM Cache C800, 16K	This option enables (turns on) or disables (turns off) the caching function of the contents of ROM area named in the option title. The settings are *Disabled* or *Enabled*
Adaptor ROM Cache CC00, 16K	This option enables (turns on) or disables (turns off) the caching function of the contents of ROM area named in the option title. The settings are *Disabled* or *Enabled*
Adaptor ROM Cache D000, 16K	This option enables (turns on) or disables (turns off) the caching function of the contents of ROM area named in the option title. The settings are *Disabled* or *Enabled*
Adaptor ROM Cache D400, 16K	This option enables (turns on) or disables (turns off) the caching function of the contents of ROM area named in the option title. The settings are *Disabled* or *Enabled*
Adaptor ROM Cache D800, 16K	This option enables (turns on) or disables (turns off) the caching function of the contents of ROM area named in the option title. The settings are *Disabled* or *Enabled*

Table 16.9 (Continued)

Adaptor ROM Cache DC00, 16K	This option enables (turns on) or disables (turns off) the caching function of the contents of ROM area named in the option title. The settings are *Disabled* or *Enabled*
Adaptor ROM Cache E000, 32K	This option enables (turns on) or disables (turns off) the caching function of the contents of ROM area named in the option title. The settings are *Disabled* or *Enabled*
Adaptor ROM Cache F000, 64K	This option enables (turns on) or disables (turns off) the caching function of the contents of ROM area named in the option title. The settings are *Disabled* or *Enabled*
LOWA20# Select	This option specifies the source of the LOWA20# signal. The settings are *KBC* or *Chipset*
RC Reset Select	This option specifies the source of the RC Rest signal. The settings are *KBC* or *Chipset*
IO Recovery Time Select	This option specifies the I/O recovery time period. The settings are *5BCLK, 7BCLK, 9BCLK, 12BCLK, 0BCLK, 1BCLK, 2BCLK* or *3BCLK*
Hold CPU Percentage	This option specifies the percentage of the full performance when non-turbo. The settings are *Disabled, 1/16, 2/16, 3/16, 4/16, 5/16, 6/16,* or *7/16*
Software Flush 80486	This option enables (turns on) or disables (turns off) the software flushing CPU internal cache when non-turbo mode. The settings are *Disabled* or *Enabled*
Enable Force Read Miss	This option enables (turns on) or disables (turns off) the forcing read miss when non-turbo mode. The settings are *Disabled* or *Enabled*

Power saving – the green PC

CMOS set-up normally offers power-saving management facilities. Also known as the green PC, power saving is achieved by reducing power consumption when the system is switched on but not being used. Power saving may be achieved by reducing the system's and CPU's clock frequencies, turning off the display unit and stopping the hard disk mechanism. Power-saving management is activated following a predefined period during which there was no activity. Normal system operation is resumed when a key is subsequently pressed or the mouse is moved. There are two power-saving modes: standby and suspend. The latter mode utilises the system management mode (SMM) provided by the 486 and Pentium processors. A typical list of options for power management set-up is given in Table 16.10.

Testing the motherboard

Following configuration and installation, the motherboard should be tested using a diagnostic routine such as PC Doctor or Microscope. This can only be carried out following a successful boot-up from a boot-up floppy or a hard disk. System memory should be tested to ensure that the total memory installed can be accessed by the computer. The processor should also be tested for a complete set of all its functions.

Table 16.10   Power management set-up

IDE Standby Power Down Mode	This option specifies the length of time of hard disk drive inactivity that must expire before the IDE hard disk drive is placed in IDE standby power down mode. The settings are *Enabled* or *Disabled*
Power Management Mode Select	This option enables (turns on) or disables (turns off) the system power management mode. The settings are *Enabled* or *Disabled*
Standby Timer Value	This option specifies the length of time of inactivity that must expire before the system is placed in standby mode. The settings are *0.5 Min., 1 Min., 2 Min., 4 Min., 8 Min., 16 Min., 32 Min., 64 Min., 128 Min., 256 Min.,* or *512 Min.*
Inactive Timer Value	This option specifies the length of time of inactivity that must expire before the system is placed in inactive mode. The settings are *2 Min., 8 Min., 32 Min., 128 Min., 512 Min., 4 Min., 16 Min., 64 Min., 256 Min.,* or *Disabled*
Sampling Activity Delay	This option specifies the delay time on sampling activity. The settings are *No Delay* or *Delay IT*
Monitor LPT Port Activity	*Enable/Disable*
Monitor COM Port Activity	*Enable/Disable*
Monitor ISA Master Activity	*Enable/Disable*
Monitor IDE Activity	*Enable/Disable*
Monitor FDC Master Activity	*Enable/Disable*
Monitor VGA Activity	*Enable/Disable*
Monitor ISA KBC Activity	*Enable/Disable*
Monitor ISA VESA Slave Activity	*Enable/Disable*
SMI# Pulse Width	This option specifies the pulse width of the system management input (SMI#) signal. The settings are *Disabled* or *Enabled*
Suspend Resume Switch	This option enables (turns on) or disables (turns off) the external suspend/resume hard switch function. The settings are *Disabled* or *Enabled*
Clock Out on Standby Mode	This option specifies the CPU clock speed when in standby. The settings are *PCLK/1, PCLK/2, PCLK/3, PCLK/4, PCLK/5, PCLK/6, PCLK/7* or *PCLK/8*
VGA Power Control	This option specifies the VGA power control method. The settings are *Disabled, VGA Off,* or *Sync. Off*
IDE Power Control	This option enables (turns on) or disables (turns off) the IDE power control function. The settings are *Disabled* or *Enabled*
APM Function	This option enables (turns on) or disables (turns off) the advanced power management (APM) function. The settings are *Disabled* or *Enabled*

17 Modems

Data communication between remote computers takes the form of sending signals along existing telephone cables using existing telephone channels. However, since a telephone channel is designed to carry analogue audio, i.e. speech signals, digital data must first be converted into a similar signal before it can be transmitted along the telephone channel. This involves modulating an audio carrier with digital data bits at one end and demodulating the carrier at the other end – hence the need for a modulator/demodulator (modem) at either end of the telephone line.

Modem operation   The basic components of a modem unit are shown in Fig. 17.1. The modem unit is connected to the data terminal equipment (DTE) such as a computer via an RS-232 serial link. Digital data from the computer is used to modulate an audio frequency carrier which may then be sent via the telephone interface along the telephone line in the same way as an ordinary speech (audio) signal. Modulated carriers from a remote computer are received by the telephone interface which directs them to the demodulator. The demodulator then translates them back into their original digital form and then sends these signals to the computer serial port via the RS-232 link. The controller manages the overall operation of the system including initialising and setting up of the operating mode and modem parameters.

When a modem is first switched on, it is initialised with one of the settings stored in a non-volatile memory (NV-RAM). This may be a default factory setting or a customised setting that has been loaded into memory. The operation and settings of the modem may be changed by special commands which the controller can execute.

When a remote modem dials in, the telephone interface detects the incoming ring and seizes the line as if it has been answered by lifting the telephone receiver. A signal is then sent to alert the PC to begin negotiating a connection. A process known as modem handshaking then commences which establishes an agreed protocol for communication and data exchange between the two modems.

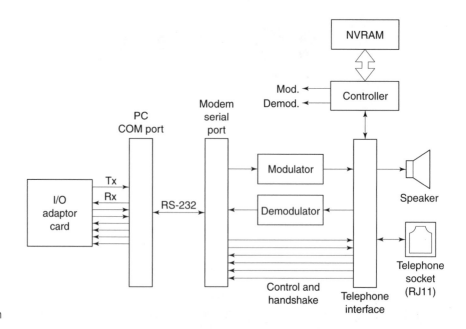

Figure 17.1 Basic components of a modem

The protocol includes an agreed speed of transmission, the size of data packets, the number signalling of bits, parity or other error correction/detection techniques. Once a protocol is agreed, the modem is set up by the controller and data exchange can commence.

The modem device normally includes a speaker which is driven by the telephone interface through which ringing and dialling tones as well as data exchange while a protocol is being negotiated are made audible to the user. The speaker is disabled during the actual transmission of data.

External and internal modems

A modem device which connects to a PC's serial port via an RS-232 link (Fig. 17.1) is known as an external modem. Such a modem is a self-contained unit separate from the PC with its own separate source of power normally through a simple transformer that plugs into the mains power socket. Alternatively, a modem device may be provided on an expansion card which plugs directly into a PC bus. Such a modem is known as an internal modem which is powered directly from the expansion bus. The other main difference is that the internal modem has its own in-built UART independent of that used by the PC's serial adaptor card.

Although the internal modem does not use one of the available serial port connectors of the PC, it must none the less be assigned a serial port number together with an appropriate COM port address. This is carried out by jumper and/or DIP switch settings provided on the expansion card as well as through software set-up procedures.

Table 17.1

Indicator	Function
AA	Auto Answer
HS	High Speed, indicating a speed of 9600 bits per second or higher
CD	Carrier Detect
OH	Off Hook (modem in control of line)
RD or RX	Receive Data (LED flickers as data is received)
SD or TX	Send Data (LED flickers as data is transmitted)
TR	Terminal Ready (LED is on when DTR signal from PC is active)
MR	Modem Ready, indicating that modem is ready
CS	Clear to Send

The port selected for the modem must of course be different from those already provided for other peripheral uses, otherwise conflict will occur resulting in the inability of the PC to recognise the modem.

One of the features of an external modem is a display of a series of LED indicators on the front panel. The LEDs provide an indication of the status of the modem at any one time. For internal modems, a similar display is sometimes included on the screen. Table 17.1 lists the typical functions of each indicator.

Modulation

Modulation is the process of using the information signal, be it analogue or digital, to change one of the properties of a carrier waveform. The modulated carrier may then be sent along a communication cable to a receiver which demodulates the carrier to extract the original signal information.

A carrier is a sinusoidal waveform with a constant amplitude, frequency and phase (Fig. 17.2a). The modulating signal, such as speech or digital data, is used to change the amplitude of the carrier (amplitude modulation (AM)), its frequency (frequency modulation (FM) or frequency shift keying (FSK)) or its phase (phase shift keying (PSK)).

A digital signal has only two states, 1 and 0, and when it is used to modulate a carrier, only two different states of the carrier amplitude, frequency or phase are necessary to convey the digital information.

In amplitude modulation (Fig 17.2b), the amplitude of the carrier is changed in accordance with the modulating signal. A high amplitude is used to represent a logic 1 and a low amplitude is used to represent logic 0. Each transition of the carrier waveform represents a single bit of data. A transmission speed of, say, 300 bps (bits per second) thus requires 300 carrier transitions per second, which is known as the baud rate of the transmission.

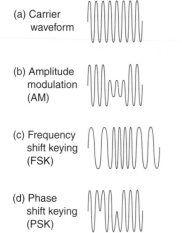

(a) Carrier waveform

(b) Amplitude modulation (AM)

(c) Frequency shift keying (FSK)

(d) Phase shift keying (PSK)

Figure 17.2 Modulation waveforms

In frequency modulation (Fig 17.2c), the carrier frequency is shifted by typically +150 Hz for logic 1 and by −150 Hz for logic 0 – hence the name frequency shift keying (FSK). As is the case with AM, each carrier transition represents 1 bit (1 bit per baud) giving a baud rate that is identical to the bps rate.

In terms of bits per baud, the most economical form of modulation is phase modulation (Fig 17.2d) known as phase shift keying (PSK) in which the carrier frequency remains constant while its phase changes in discrete phase states in accordance with the logic state of the data bit. Binary PSK is a two-phase modulation technique in which the carrier is transmitted with a phase of 0° to indicate a logic 1 and a phase of 180° to indicate logic 0. Once again each bit is represented by one carrier transition resulting in 1 bit per baud. The number of bits per baud may be increased using smaller phase increments such as 90° for a four-phase or 45° for an eight-phase PSK.

The four-phase, quadrature phase shift keying (QPSK) has four phase settings: a reference 0° phase, 90°, 180° and 270°. Each setting is used to represent the instantaneous states of a pair of bits which can take one of four combinations, namely 00, 01, 10 and 11. Each of these combinations changes the phase of the carrier from its previous setting by a different angle as shown in Table 17.2. The four 2-bit data combinations are thus represented by four different phase changes. For example, data 00 is represented by no change in the phase of the carrier, 01 is represented by a 90° phase shift and 10 is represented by a 180° phase change as shown in Table 17.2. Fig. 17.3 shows a PSK modulated carrier waveform.

The advantage of this type of modulation is its ability to send twice as much information as the binary PSK, namely 2 bits per baud. The transmission rate is therefore twice the baud rate. A 1200 baud modem using a binary PSK modulation therefore has a transfer rate of $2 \times 1200 = 2400$ bps.

Further improvements in bits per baud may be obtained using quadrature amplitude modulation in which both the phase and amplitude of the carrier are changed to encode more than 2 bits per baud. Trellis-coded quadrature amplitude modulation (TCQAM), also known as trellis-coded modulation (TCM), uses 6 bits per baud for a transfer rate of 14,400 or over.

Table 17.2

b1	b0	Phase angle
0	0	0°
0	1	90°
1	0	180°
1	1	270°

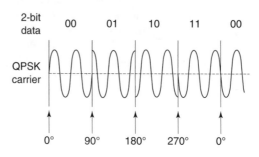

Figure 17.3 Quadrature PSK modulated carrier

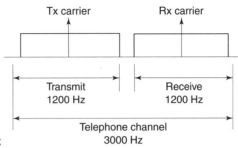

Figure 17.4 Frequency division multiplex

Bandwidth and baud rate

The bandwidth allocated for a telephone channel is 3 kHz (300 Hz to 3300 Hz). A data communication channel using the telephone system must therefore fit within this bandwidth.

In general data signals will be flowing in both directions. This is called duplex operation. It is full duplex if communication can take place in both directions simultaneously and half duplex if data can only flow in one direction at a time.

Where full duplex operation is used, the bandwidth of the telephone channel must be shared between the two-way signals using frequency division multiplex (FDM) as shown in Fig. 17.4. Two different carrier frequencies are used, one for the transmit, Tx, channel and the second for the receive, Rx, channel. These frequencies are generated by the appropriate modems. The modem originating the transmission generates the carrier for Tx and the modem receiving the transmission generates the carrier for Rx. Each carrier is then modulated by the appropriate digital data and sent along the telephone line.

To ensure the integrity of two-way communication, a gap is inserted between the two modulated signals (Fig. 17.4). This reduces the total available bandwidth to 2400 Hz, i.e. 1200 Hz for each of the Tx and the Rx signals. This means that the maximum frequency that can be accommodated for a full duplex operation is 1200 Hz. Maximum frequency is obtained when the transitions of the carrier alternate between 1 and 0 as shown in Fig. 17.5. One cycle of the waveform thus represents two transitions (or bits). It therefore follows that the rate of carrier transitions, i.e. the baud rate, is twice the bandwidth giving a maximum baud rate of $2 \times 1200 = 2400$. The actual bit rate is determined by the number of bits each carrier transition represents. For a 1 bit per baud operation, the maximum bit rate is 2400 bps. Using QPSK, the bit rate may be doubled to 4800 bps and so on. This is the reason why modem speed is a multiple of 2400 bps.

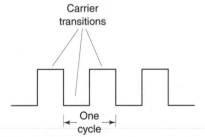

Figure 17.5 Maximum frequency is produced with alternating 0s and 1s

Increasing data throughput

There are two techniques which may be used to improve the throughput of data without increasing the bps rate of transfer: synchronous transmission and data compression. By using the synchronous mode of transmission, the additional bits associated with the asynchronous mode, namely the start and stop bits, may be dispensed with. All of the bits are data bits resulting in improvement of the throughput by up to 30 per cent. Data compression examines groups of data and generates coded messages to describe them. In its simplest form, it removes repetitive data and replaces it with the data itself and the number of times it repeats itself, a process requiring far fewer bits.

Modem commands

Modern modems are intelligent devices which can execute a number of sophisticated instructions in the form of ASCII text commands. Although there is no standard set of modem commands, the Hayes AT command set is the acceptable standard throughout the industry.

Virtually all AT commands start with the prefix AT (attention) followed by one command or a string of commands. For example to instruct the modem to dial 2085000, the following string is entered:

ATDT2085000

where AT is attention, D dial, T tone dialling, followed by the telephone number.

Following the execution of a command or a command string, the modem responds by a statement indicating status, such as OK, CONNECTING, etc.

S-Registers

Programming a modem involves setting its operating features and parameters. The modem provides a number of 8-bit registers known as S-Registers which are used for this purpose. The original Hayes modem specified 28 such registers (S0–S27) for different functions such as the number of rings before answering, type of handshake and baud rate. Later modems have included a larger number of S-Registers to accommodate expanded features and applications. There are two types of S-Registers: the integer or numeric and the bit-mapped register. The integer type defines a specific parameter, e.g. S0, which sets the number of rings before answering, and S10, which determines the duration before the modem hangs up following a loss of carrier. Such a register contains a numeric value between 0 and 255. In the bit-mapped register, each bit acts independently determining a particular feature of the modem, such as S13.

The contents of the S-Registers are set during the initialisation stage of the modem. These settings may be changed if a different initialisation command string is used or by Hayes modem command Sr = n, where r is the register number and n is the new value to be entered.

Command and communication modes

A modem can operate in one of two modes: the command mode and the communication mode, also known as the data mode. In the command mode, the modem receives and carries out AT commands such as dial a number, hang up or change the value of an S-Register. In the communication mode, the modem acts as a data processing device for uploading and downloading data files along a telephone line to and from a remote computer or terminal. When in the command mode, a modem is switched over to the communication mode by an instruction from the computer. When in the communication mode, the modem is unable to respond to an instruction. Switching back to the command mode must therefore involve sending a combination of characters which the modem would interpret as an instruction to revert back to the command mode. The most widely used method of switching from the communication mode to the command mode is halting the data flow for a specified period of time known as a 'guard period', followed by a set of characters that is unlikely to be found in normal data communication, such as +++, followed by a second 'guard period'.

File transfer protocols

Before data is exchanged between modems, a protocol must be established. Such a protocol will specify the transfer mode as well as the type of error detection and correction if any. There are several standard protocols which modems may be programmed to utilise: ASCII, Xmodem, Ymodem, Zmodem and Kermit.

ASCII

Designed for text files, the ASCII protocol uses X-ON/X-OFF flow control with no error checking; this is useful for uninterrupted bursts of raw data.

Xmodem

Xmodem employs asynchronous data transfer (8 bits, no parity and one stop bit) with no restrictions on contents of files. Data is divided into small blocks or packets of 128 bytes each with a simple checksum byte added to each packet for error detection. When a packet is successfully received, the receiving end sends back an acknowledge (ACK) byte. If unsuccessful, the receiving end sends a non-acknowledge (NAK) byte which causes the packet to be retransmitted. Long delays may be experienced with this method but are avoided with the windowed Xmodem (WXmodem) which assumes successful transmission and checks for unsuccessfully transmitted packets at the end of the session and proceeds to re-transmit them.

Xmodem CRC

This protocol improves error detection by using a 16-bit cyclic redundancy count (CRC) which provides almost 100 per cent data accuracy and integrity.

Xmodem 1K

This protocol replaces the 128-byte packet with a 1024(1K)-byte packet thus improving the speed of file transfer.

Ymodem

Also known as Ymodem-Batch, Ymodem-1K and Ymodem-CRC, this protocol is an improved version of the Xmodem 1K protocol transmitting (1KB packets with CRC error detection). However, unlike Xmodem 1K, the Ymodem protocol can automatically receive or send multiple files (including individual filenames) with a single instruction in one session of transmission.

Ymodem-G

This is a variant of the Ymodem protocol designed to be used with modems that provide error correction. It sends and receives 1KB packets of data as a continuous stream until instructed to stop. If any packet is interrupted, the entire transfer is cancelled and must be resumed from the beginning.

Zmodem

The Zmodem protocol is a very efficient data transfer protocol which provides for multiple file exchange in a single transfer together with filenames, sizes and dates. Like Ymodem-G, the Zmodem protocol transfers 1KB packets of data in quick succession. At the end of the session, it pools for unsuccessful packets, identified by non-acknowledge (NAK) signals and re-transmits them. However, unlike Ymodem-G, the Zmodem protocol may, following a crash or interruption, resume the transfer from where it was suspended.

Kermit

Named after the frog, the Kermit protocol is designed for data transfer between computers of different types such as mainframes, miniframes and PCs. Kermit can use different-sized data packets of up to 1KB.

Modem standards   Before communication between two modems can commence, they have to establish a common communication protocol. A number of standard protocols for modems have been set up. They fall into two categories: the Microcom Networking Protocol (MNP), such as MNP Class 2 and MNP Class 3, and the Comité Consultatif International Télégraphique et Téléphonique (International Telegraph and Telephone Consultative Committee) (CCITT), such as V.32 and V.42. The following are some of the more popular MNP standards:

MNP Class 4. Employs error correction and a limited amount of data compression. It uses a technique called adaptive packet assembly which tests the telephone line and sends larger data packets on noise-free lines. Throughput is increased by 20 per cent to achieve a throughput of 1450 bps from a 1200 bps modem.

MNP Class 5. A purely data compression protocol, this can squeeze data by a factor of up to two.

MNP Class 6. This protocol is designed to get the best out of a telephone connection. Using a technique called universal link negotiations, modems can gradually increase their speed up to the optimum possible for the particular line.

MNP Class 7. By using a more efficient compression algorithm, a compression factor of up to three is possible with this protocol.

MNP Class 9. This protocol reduces overhead bits and improves error correction with only erroneous data being retransmitted.

MNP Class 10. Using a technique called adverse channel enhancements, this protocol adjusts the data packet size to accommodate poor connection. It is a more powerful version of MNP4.

The CCITT standards provide specifications for different protocols. Table 17.3 lists some of the more popular standards.

Table 17.3

Standard	Function
V.22	1200 bps at 600 baud using PSK
V.22bis	2400 bps at 600 baud using QAM
V.32	High speed data transfer of 4800 and 9600 bps at a baud rate of 2400 using QAM
V.32bis	Extends the V.32 to 4800, 7200, 12,000 and 14,400 bps at the same 2400 baud rate using TCQAM
V.32terbo	16,800, 19,200 bps with a baud rate of 2400
V.32fast	28,800 bps with 2400 baud rate
V.42	Error correction specification for V.32 and V.32bis incorporating MNP4
V.42bis	Error correction specification similar to but incompatible with MNP5 and MNP7

Fax-modems   The concept of facsimile (fax) transmission was patented as early as 1842. It has been extensively used in the newspaper transmission of photographs on telephone lines. A fax machine consists of a scanner which divides a page of script or graphics into a number of lines and converts them into a stream of data bits, line by line, in a form that can be transmitted on a telephone channel. The process is reversed at the receiving end where the page is reconstructed, line by line, and reproduced as hard copy by a printer.

In the case of a fax-modem, a software program is used to convert text or images (or even files) stored in the computer into standard facsimile format for fax transmission. Neither a scanner nor paper is necessary. At the receiving end another fax-modem is used to capture the image into a graphic file. A hard copy may be produced by an appropriate print command. Fax-modems can of course send and receive transmissions to and from fax machines.

Group 1 and 2 fax protocols employed analogue technology using FSK modulation. The baud rate was limited to 300. A full page of information took 6 minutes to transmit. Digital technology was introduced by the Group 3 protocol which used data compression to raise the bps rating to 14,400. Under this protocol, two levels of resolution are available: standard with 220×200 dots per inch (dpi) and fine which doubles the vertical resolution to 400 dpi. With the fine resolution, transmission time is also doubled. The Group 4 protocol improved the resolution up to 400×400 dpi with increased speeds at lower resolutions.

ISDN   The Integrated Services Digital Network (ISDN) is an all-digital communication system using existing telephone lines. Being a fully digital system, ISDN dispenses with the modem. In its place a terminal adaptor (TA) is used as an interface between the computer and the telephone network. External terminal adaptors connect to one of the PC COM ports and internal terminal adaptors are allocated a COM port in the same way as are internal modems. Terminal adaptors accept the AT commands thus allowing communication application programs to use standard Hayes commands.

ISDN provides a total bandwidth of 144 kbits/s employing a simple two-wire configuration. The most popular ISDN service is the Basic Rate Interface (BRI) which provides services to offices and homes. This service divides the 144 kbits/s bandwidth into two 64 kbits/s channels known as bearer (B) channels and a third 16 kbits/s D channel. The B channels carry voice, data and fax information while the D channel is used for set-up and control.

With a bandwidth of 64 kbits/s, twice that of the analogue modem, each B channel can deliver a significantly higher data throughput which may be improved using data compression. The other advantage of the ISDN is its capacity to handle existing analogue equipment alongside ISDN devices.

18 Multimedia: CD-ROM and sound card

A multimedia PC (MPC) is a computer with certain minimum standards as to the size of memory, the type of processor, the type of hard disk and video display together with a CD-ROM drive with sound capabilities. Multimedia may also support full motion video capabilities.

The CD-ROM

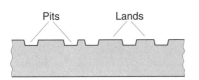

Figure 18.1 The CD-ROM disk surface

The compact disc read only memory (CD-ROM) is a high capacity storage device based on the same optical technology as the ordinary audio CD. Digital information is stored in the form of tiny depressions known as pits made on the surface of the disc (Fig. 18.1). A pit may thus represent a logic 0 and an absence of a pit, known as a land, may represent a logic 1. The digital information is engraved along a single spiral track stretching from the inner circle to the outer rim of the disc.

Reading the disc involves the use of a laser beam aimed at a reflective mirror. By precision-controlled rotation of the mirror, the laser beam can be made to follow the spiral track and examine any part of the rotating disc (Fig. 18.2). If the beam hits a pit, the beam is scattered and the reflection is weak. However, when the beam hits a flat surface, i.e. a land, a high intensity reflection is obtained. The sensor receives the deflected beams and detects the intensity of the reflected beam converting the pit and lands into zeros and ones.

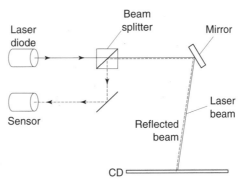

Figure 18.2 Simplified construction of a CD-ROM drive

Data organisation

A CD-ROM is a very efficient mass storage device. The relatively small compact disc, 120 mm across, has a data capacity exceeding 600MB, which is equivalent to the capacity of a few hundred floppy disks. A CD-ROM divides the data into sectors (also known as blocks) consisting of 2352 bytes. Of these, 2048 bytes are actual information data bits, 4 bytes are allocated for synchronisation, 12 bytes for addressing and 288 bytes for error correction. With data compression, the disk capacity can be considerably increased.

Having developed from the audio CD, the CD-ROM is assigned a length of 'playtime'. A total of 79 minutes of playtime is available although most manufacturers limit this to 60 minutes with the first minute assigned for track ID information. In 60 minutes, 270,000 sectors or blocks are written. With 2048 bytes or 2KB per sector, the total capacity of 60 minutes of playtime is

$$270,000 \times 2 = 540,000\text{KB or}$$
$$540,000/1024 = 527.3\text{MB}$$

If all the 79 minutes of playtime were used, a total capacity of 681MB would be obtained.

Data transfer rate

For a total capacity of 527.3MB recorded over 60 minutes, the data transfer rate may be calculated as follows:

$$527.3 \times 1024 = 540,000\text{KB per 60 minutes}$$
$$= 540,000/60 = 9000\text{KB per minute}$$
$$= 9000/60 = 150\text{KB per second}$$

A faster transfer rate may be obtained with multi-speed drives. A double speed ($2\times$) drive achieves a transfer rate of $2 \times 150 = 300$KB/s, and triple speed drives ($3\times$) a transfer rate of $3 \times 150 = 450$KB/s and so on. Drives with speeds of $8\times$ and $10\times$ are available giving transfer rates of 1200KB/s and 1500KB/s respectively.

Access time

Compared with a hard disk drive with a typical access time of 10 ms, the CD-ROM has a very slow access time of between 100 and 300 ms. The reasons for the long access time are twofold: the physical size of the optical head and the differential rotational angular velocity of the disc. Compared with the R/W head of a hard disk drive, the optical head of a CD-ROM drive is much more massive. The CD-ROM drive mechanism thus has more mass to move which takes a longer time to shift from one position to another. Secondly, while the hard disk rotates at a constant angular speed (300 revolutions per minute), the compact disc rotates at differential angular speed in order to keep the scanning speed of the track and hence data throughout constant. As the optical head moves from a sector near the outside rim of the disc to another nearer its centre, the motor must accelerate to achieve the new speed required to maintain a constant rate of data throughput. In the 1× mode with a data throughout of 150KB/s, a CD-ROM changes its speed from 200 to 600 revolutions per minute as the head moves from the rim to the centre. Faster drives require a greater range of speeds. Time is required for the servo mechanism to react to such variations in speed, adding to the access time of the CD drive.

The CD-ROM drive

The basic components of a CD-ROM drive are shown in Fig. 18.3. The digital data produced by the optical head is decoded and fed into a buffer memory before going to the adaptor card via an interface. The operation is controlled by a controller which among other things directs the movement of the laser beam and controls the speed of the precision servo motor as the head moves from one data sector to another.

The buffer memory is actual chips installed on the drive which allows large amounts of data to be stored before it is sent to the PC. The faster the speed of the drive, the larger the buffer size that is necessary to handle the higher transfer rates. A typical buffer size is 256KB.

The interface provides the communication between the CD-ROM and the adaptor card which slots into the motherboard. There are three types of interfaces available: SCSI/ASPI, IDE/ATAPI and proprietary. The last one is non-standard and product specific.

The SCSI/ASPI (Advanced SCSI Programming Interface) is the most commonly used software to communicate between the CD drive and the computer. It offers greater flexibility and easier

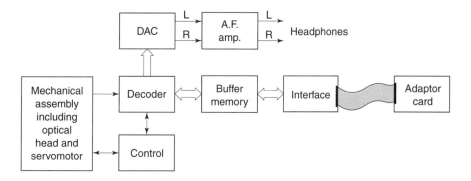

Figure 18.3 CD-ROM drive block diagram

configuration than the other two types. The CD drive is assigned one of the seven device numbers or addresses available by the SCSI adaptor provided it has not been assigned to another peripheral. The IDE/ATAPI (AT Attachment Packet Interface) is the same interface as that used for hard disks. The ATAPI is an industry standard enhanced IDE interface for CD-ROM drives using software which adapts the SCSI/ASPI commands to the IDE/ATA interface used for hard drives. The same DOS routine, MSCDEX, may thus be used for both SCSI/ASPI and IDE-supported CD-ROM drives. Normally, a second IDE adaptor interface and cable are used, separate from those used for the hard disk. Jumpers on the adaptor card set the IRQ number, the port address and the DMA channel. As usual, conflicts between peripherals must be avoided. Typically, IRQ15, DMA channel 5 and port address 0300H or 0220H are used. Other port addresses that are normally available are 0330H and 0200H.

CD-ROM drives provide a stereophonic audio output which may be used for playing audio CDs. The output from the decoder is fed into an 8- or 16-bit digital-to-analogue converter (DAC) which provides a stereophonic output, Left and Right. Following amplification, the output is made available on a headphone jack.

Software requirements

A CD-ROM requires two software routines for its operation: a CD-ROM device driver to access the device and a Microsoft routine, MSCDEX.EXE, to read the stored files. Where a SCSI is used, a further SCSI device driver must also be installed.

The device driver is provided by the manufacturer and must be loaded into CONFIG.SYS. A typical arrangement is

DEVICE=C:\PATH\CDROM.SYS /D:LABEL

where

PATH	indicates the directory/subdirectory where the driver routine is to be located, e.g. \CDROM\DRIVERS
CDROM.SYS	is the CD-ROM driver specific to the CD-ROM drive provided by the manufacturer
D:LABEL	is the drive/label or number, typically D:MSCD000 or D:MSCD001 (any other label may be used, e.g. D:KFI000)

Microsoft developed an extension to MS-DOS that provides a standard method of accessing the CD-ROM. Called Microsoft CD-ROM Extension, MSCDEX.EXE, this routine may be loaded and run from the DOS prompt. More usually it is included in AUTOEXEC.BAT.

A typical command line is

C:\DOS\MSCDEX.EXE /D:/MSCD000

where

C:\DOS	is the path
MSCDEX.EXE	is the name of the DOS extension
D:/MSCD000	is the drive/label or number used for the device driver (any other label may be used provided it is the same as that used for the device driver, e.g. D:MSCD001)

MSCDEX has a number of other switches all of which are optional:

/L specifies the drive letter to assign the first CD (default is D:)
/M specifies the number of sector buffers
/E allows the use of expanded memory for buffers
/K supports Japanese (Kanji)
/S enables sharing of the CD-ROM with other work groups or
    networks
/V displays the above information

For Windows 95, an in-built CD file system (CDFS) driver takes the place of MSCDEX.EXE.

Once the drive has been installed and the software loaded and run, access to the CD-ROM is achieved by selecting the specified drive, normally D:.

The sound card

Sound is a variation of air pressure produced by, for example, speech, loudspeakers, musical instruments or pneumatic drills. Sound travels through the air in the form of waves of varying frequencies. The amplitude of the wave determines its volume or loudness and its frequency determines its tone or pitch. The range of sound frequencies that can be heard by the human ear, the audio frequency (a.f.) range, extends from 20 Hz to 20 kHz, although 15 kHz is the highest most people can hear.

Electronic sound processing involves using a microphone to transform the sound waves into electrical signals which, following amplification or any other electronic manipulation, are transformed back into sound waves using a loudspeaker (Fig. 18.4). Where the process involves the use of a digital system such as a computer, the analogue signals at the input must be changed into digital signals using an analogue-to-digital converter (ADC) and vice versa at the other end using a digital-to-analogue converter (DAC) as shown in Fig. 18.5. The two converters are normally incorporated on a single IC known as a code–decode or CODEC chip.

The ADC takes the analogue input, samples it and then converts the amplitude of each sample into a digital code (Fig. 18.6). The output is

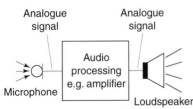

Figure 18.4 Analogue sound processing

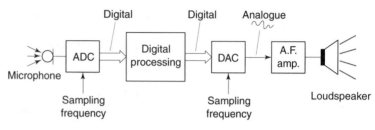

Figure 18.5 Digital sound processing

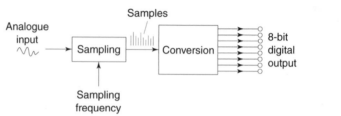

Figure 18.6 Analogue-to-digital conversion (ADC)

a number of parallel bits (eight in Fig. 18.6) whose simultaneous logic states represent the level of each sample in turn. Shannon theory states that for satisfactory results, the analogue signal must be sampled at a minimum rate of twice the highest frequency of the input. For high quality audio, the highest frequency is 20 kHz, which gives a sampling rate of $2 \times 20 = 40$ kHz. In practice, the minimum sampling rate is increased by about 10 per cent to prevent interference caused by frequency overlap. This results in a standard sampling rate of 44.1 kHz which is also the sampling rate of CD quality audio. The number of bits produced by the ADC determines its resolution and hence the precision by which the level of each sample is represented. An 8-bit converter provides $2^8 = 256$ different levels, which is adequate for normal speech. However, for hi-fi CD quality sound a 16-bit (65,536 levels) converter is necessary.

Computer sound system

The main components of a sound card are shown in Fig. 18.7. Modern PC sound systems centre around a special purpose dedicated processor called the digital signal processor (DSP). The DSP has a special architecture with an instruction set designed to process analogue information that has been converted to digital. It can free the main processor from a number of time-consuming tasks such as filtering and data compression and decompression as well as performing special effects and providing music synthesis. The ROM contains all the instructions and the routines necessary to operate the DSP. It may also contain data for sound clips which may be called by the DSP and processed through the synthesiser. A small RAM chip is usually made available for storing temporary sound data.

The sound card adaptor can process and store audio signals directly from a microphone or from other audio equipment.

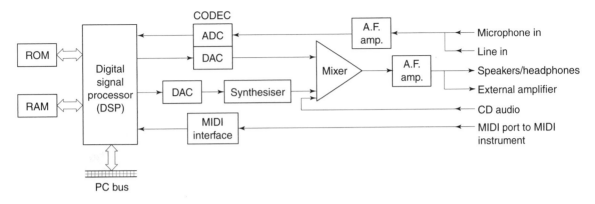

Figure 18.7   The sound card – block diagram

Following amplification, these signals are converted to digital format by the ADC and processed by the DSP. They may then be stored as a waveform audio (WAV) file on a floppy or a hard disk.

The most popular application of a sound adaptor is the reproduction of sound generated by application programs. Digitally coded sound arrives at the DSP via the motherboard expansion slot. It is processed and fed into a DAC before going into the mixer. The mixer receives audio signals from a number of sources, controls their individual levels and mixes them to create a common stereo output.

The Musical Instrument Digital Interface (MIDI) is an asynchronous serial interface (similar to a serial port) which provides a facility for replicating the sounds of a variety of musical instruments such as piano, guitar or flute. Also known as a MIDI Processing Unit (MPU-401 UART), the MIDI interface uses the synthesiser to reproduce the notes of selected instruments. The midi keyboard selects the note to be produced and sends it to the DSP via the midi interface. It is processed and sent to the synthesiser via a DAC. Each note is produced by a specific synthesiser program which is invoked by coded commands sent by the MIDI instrument. The General MIDI standard defines 128 program codes or pages which have been accepted by most manufacturers of sound cards. Because the synthesisers can process several channels simultaneously, the General MIDI standard supports the playing of a number of instruments called voices at the same time. Music produced in this way may be stored in the form of MIDI program codes, saving on disk space.

The 15-pin D-shell MIDI port may also be used as a game port or for a joystick. One or two game controllers may be connected to the port, each with an X and Y position control capability, together with a total of four switches or fire buttons.

Sound WAV files

WAV files may occupy a very large section of disk space depending on the sampling rate and converter resolution. For instance, the amount of disk space required to store 1 minute of 16-bit digitised stereophonic sound at a sampling rate of 44.1 kHz may be calculated as follows:

Data flow per channel = 44.1 kHz × 16 bits = 705.6 kbits/s
Data flow rate for both channels = 2 × 705.6 = 1411.2 kbits/s = 1411.2/8 = 176.4KB/s
Data flow per minute = 176.4 × 60 = 10,584 MB

The amount of disk space may be reduced by using data compression. For instance, companding, used in NICAM television sound, can reduce the actual number of bits without affecting the resolution. Additive differential pulse code modulation (ADPCM) can compress data by a factor of up to four. Motion Picture Expert Group (MPEG) is another highly effective compression specification with a potential compression factor of up to 12.

Synthesisers

Synthesised sound is electronically composed and electronically generated sound. There are several synthesis techniques including frequency modulation (FM) and wave table synthesis.

FM synthesis utilises the fact that a musical note is composed of a number of pure sine waves added to each other. FM synthesis technology involves the generation of sine waves of varying amplitude and frequencies using special chips or DSPs. These sine waves are added to produce the required sounds. In the wave table synthesis technique, small representative segments or samples of real sound waveforms that have been digitised are stored in a look-up table. When an instrument is to be synthesised, its stored segments are accessed and processed by a wave table synthesiser, which is usually a DSP chip. Because the stored segments are real sound waveforms, a more realistic simulated sound is generated. The instrument's segment data is called a patch set and is normally stored in a special ROM chip. Patch memory sizes vary between 512KB and 4MB depending on the number of instruments supported and whether data compression is used. Wave table synthesisers are capable of playing multiple instruments simultaneously which are combined by a mixer to produce a single stereo output.

The sound blaster

The sound blaster is not, as the name may suggest, a type of 'ghetto blaster'. It is a standardised combination of PC sound processing and

FM synthesis. The accepted standard for sound blaster cards is that set by Creative Laboratories. Based around Yamaha's chipset, the sound blaster may have increased capabilities with the inclusion of a creative sound processor (CSP) (also known as advance signal processor (ASP)).

Sound card installation

Most sound cards not only provide realistic stereo sound but can also support a CD-ROM. Fig. 18.8 shows a typical sound card adaptor with a CD-ROM IDE interface connector. A number of jumpers are provided which among other things allow the setting of the I/O port base address, the IRQ number and the DMA channel. A typical set of jumpers is listed in Table 18.1.

A number of connectors are provided at the back of the face plate of the adaptor card, including a stereo line input for external audio equipment, e.g. audio CD, a microphone socket, a stereo line out for audio amplification, a speaker/headphone jack for sound output without amplification and a 15-pin D-shell connector for a MIDI synthesiser or a joystick.

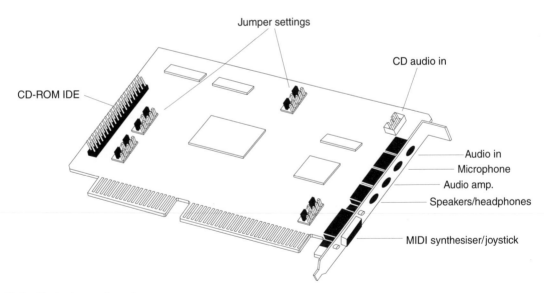

Figure 18.8   Typical sound card

Table 18.1

Jumper	Default	Options
IRQ	15	10, 11
I/O port address	220H or 330H	240H
DMA channel	DMA5	None available
Microphone type	Condenser	Carbon

Before installing the adaptor card, a check should be made to ensure that the default configuration (IRQ, I/O port address, DMA channel) of the sound card does not conflict with other installed adaptors. Microsoft Diagnostic (MSD) or other diagnostic programs may be used to ascertain the allocation of IRQs, I/O port addresses and DMA channels. Where these overlap with the default setting of the sound card, a different setting must be selected.

Following the hardware configuration, the software provided by the manufacturer must then be loaded. This is usually achieved by running a special INSTALL or SETUP file which will install the necessary software and update CONFIG.SYS and AUTOEXEC.BAT where necessary.

19 Logical fault finding

Fault finding must follow a logical sequence, the purpose of which is to identify the cause of the fault and then rectify it. The number of tests should be kept to a minimum, and unnecessary or pointless tests must be avoided. Care must be taken to ensure that the process of fault finding does not itself cause damage, introduce further faults or create conditions for potential component failure in the future. For this reason strict precautions must be taken at all times.

The process of fault finding begins with turning on the computer and observing what happens. A 'dead' computer points to a power supply, system clock or reset failure, otherwise a boot-up process commences which among other things performs a number of checks to test the integrity of the system. These checks include a series of self-tests as well as an examination of the system's set-up and configuration. The PC, being an intelligent device, uses these checks to display basic information on the system's configuration and generates error messages and beeps if necessary. A vast amount of information on the working condition of the system may be gained from these early checks, which is indispensable for fault finding.

There are a number of diagnostic aids available on the market, all of which are useful to varying degrees. However, the best aid is a good knowledge of the workings of the system and a logical approach to fault finding.

Precautions

There are two types of precautions that must be taken before any attempt is made to inspect a computer for faults: software or anti-virus and hardware or anti-static precautions.

Anti-virus precautions

A virus is an unwanted computer fragment of an instruction code or a program which can replicate itself into other areas and causes loss of data or degradation of a program. Apart from program failures and loss of data, viruses may also cause malfunction symptoms which are very similar to those produced by other software or hardware faults. For this reason, viruses must be isolated and removed before any attempt at fault finding is made. MS-DOS and other software makers provide anti-virus routines which must be used to create a virus-free working area. This involves checking for viruses in the PC by scanning all its components including memory and hard disk, as well as checking all floppy disks before they are used.

Anti-static precautions

The movement and contact of the human body can accumulate energy in the form of electrostatic charge. When an electric contact is established, electrostatic discharge (ESD) takes place in the form of a very brief flow of current. Although the discharge current is very small, the voltage could be in the region of few thousand volts. Such an electrostatic discharge can cause damage to MOS-based integrated circuits such as CMOS and NMOS and other memory chips. The damage caused by ESD may be instant failure. However, it is more likely to weaken the chip thus shortening its life span. Anti-static precautions involve taking the following steps:

- the use of a grounded wrist strap designed for static discharge or, alternatively, touching a grounded metal when handling cards and components;
- handling the boards by their edges only and avoiding touching their components;
- when handling components, avoiding touching the pins;
- the use of an anti-static work surface or mat which ensures that all parts of its surface are kept at the same potential;
- keeping all system and other boards as well as peripherals in anti-static bags when not in use;
- touching a grounded metal object when removing a board from its anti-static bag;
- making sure that the system's chassis provides good ground contact between its power supply, case, mounting fasteners and the motherboard.

Boot-up failure

Table 19.1 lists the sequence of events, stage by stage, of the boot-up process following a system power-up. The point at which the boot-up process is halted provides a very good indication of the cause of the malfunction. The point at which failure occurs may be deduced by careful observation of the symptoms including any displayed messages and listening to sounds and beep codes.

Stage 1 failure – the 'dead' computer

A 'dead' computer with a normally functioning cooling fan suggests a power supply, system clock or reset failure, or a short circuit on the

Table 19.1

Stage 1	The cooling fan rotates as the power supply d.c. voltages build up to their normal level. The hard disk also begins to rotate making a slight whirring sound.
Stage 2	Power on self-test (POST) routines are performed by BIOS:

(i) Motherboard test including processor and other support chips. Coded beeps indicate errors

(ii) Video adaptor test. A successful test is indicated by a cursor or some display on the screen and errors are indicated by coded beeps

(iii) Memory test. The total size of system memory is usually indicated when test is completed

(iv) Peripheral tests. These include the hard and floppy disk as well as the CD-ROM drives together with the serial and parallel ports, the keyboard and the mouse. Flashing LEDs indicate a device test. Errors may be reported in the form of coded beeps or written messages on the screen

(v) A single beep is generated indicating a successful series of tests

Stage 3	System configuration displayed on the screen. The actual information provided depends on the manufacturer of the ROM BIOS, its version and date. Two different configuration displays (AMI and Award) are shown in Fig. 19.1.
Stage 4	Operating system loaded. The usual boot-up sequence is A:;C:. The sequence is indicated by flashing indicator LEDs.
Stage 5	CONFIG.SYS and AUTOEXEC.BAT files are executed in that order
Stage 6	MS-DOS prompt is displayed on the screen

motherboard, an expansion card or a peripheral. There is no particular order in which the test should be carried out. It is a matter of preference and intuition.

The outputs of the power supply could be tested first. The best place to do this is at the power connection at the motherboard. Correct voltage levels including the power good line indicate a good power unit.

The system clock may be checked at B30 of one of the ISA slots using a logic probe. Where a reset button is available, its operation may be quickly tested by disconnecting it from the motherboard. Otherwise, a voltmeter should be used to measure the voltage as the computer is reset or rebooted.

If the power is suspected, the power cables supplying the motherboard, the HDD, the FDD and other peripherals should be removed one by one. Every time one set of cables is removed, the power should be turned on and the d.c. voltages tested. In carrying out d.c. measurements, at least one set of power cables must remain

```
┌─────────────────────────────────────────────────────────────────────────┐
│   AMIBIOS System Configuration (C) 1985-1994, American Megatrends Inc.,   │
│                                                                           │
│  Main Processor    : 80486DX2        Base Memory Size   : 640KB           │
│  Numeric Processor : Built-In        Ext. Memory Size   : 3072KB          │
│  Floppy Drive A:   : 1.44 MB 3½"     Display Type        : VGA/EGA        │
│  Floppy Drive B:   : None            Serial Port(s)      : 3F8,2F8        │
│  AMIBIOS Date      : 10/10/94        Parallel Port(s)    : 378            │
│  ─────────────────────────────────────────────────────────────────────  │
│  Hard Disk(s)            Cyl   Hd  Sec  Size    LBA  32Bit Block  PIO     │
│                                                  Mode Mode  Mode  Mode    │
│  Primary Master    : C:  1024  12  34   204MB   Off  Off   16Sec  3       │
└─────────────────────────────────────────────────────────────────────────┘
```

```
                           Award Software, Inc.
                           System Configurations

┌─────────────────────────────────────────────────────────────────────────┐
│  CPU Type          : 80486DX2-S      Base Memory      :    640K           │
│  Co-Processor      : Installed       Extended Memory  :   7168K           │
│  CPU Clock         : 66MHz           Cache Memory     :    256K           │
│  ─────────────────────────────────────────────────────────────────────  │
│  Diskette Drive  A : 1.44M, 3.5 in.  Display Type      : EGA/VGA          │
│  Diskette Drive  B : None            Serial Port(s)    : 3F8 2F8          │
│  Pri. Master  Disk : Mode 1,   272MB Parallel Port(s)  : 278              │
│  Pri. Slave   Disk : None                                                 │
│  Sec. Master  Disk : None                                                 │
│  Sec. Slave   Disk : None                                                 │
└─────────────────────────────────────────────────────────────────────────┘
```

Figure 19.1 Two practical system configuration displays

connected to either the motherboard or a peripheral. The process should be repeated, only this time by removing the expansion cards, one at a time. By a process of elimination, the faulty unit can easily be detected. Otherwise, the power unit should be replaced by a known-good unit with the same power specification.

Cooling fan failure

A failure of the cooling fan to rotate may be detected by the absence of turning noise as well as the absence of air flow at the back of the computer. A failed cooling fan heats the power unit causing a thermal cut-out to operate and power cuts off with the computer rendered 'dead'. The electric fan may be checked by connecting a 12 V d.c. supply to its terminals. If the fan is found to be in working order, then the cause may be a faulty motherboard, adaptor card or a peripheral. The process of removing the power cable from the motherboard and peripherals, one at a time, should be repeated. Before the power unit is finally replaced, the mains power cable and the mains fuse should be checked.

Stage 2 failure – POST error codes   Faults associated with the power on self-test (POST) are generally indicated by one or more types of error messages. Error messages come in three possible forms: audible beeps, I/O POST codes and

Table 19.2 AMIBIOS beep codes

Beeps	Message	Description
1	POST Test Successful	
2	Parity Error	Parity error in the first 64KB of memory
3	Base 64 KB Memory Failure	Memory failure in the first 64KB
4	Timer Not Operational	Memory failure in the first 64KB of memory, or Timer 1 on the mother-board is not functioning
5	Processor Error	The CPU on the board generated an error
6	8042 – Gate A20 Failure	The keyboard controller may be bad. The BIOS cannot switch to protected mode
7	Processor Exception Interrupt Error	The CPU generated an exception interrupt
8	Display Memory Read/Write Error	The system video adaptor is missing or its memory is faulty. This is not a fatal error
9	ROM Checksum Error	The ROM checksum value does not match the value encoded in the BIOS
10	CMOS Shutdown Register Read/Write Error	The shutdown register for CMOS RAM failed
11	Cache Error/External Cache Bad	The external cache is faulty

displayed messages. The last ones require a video card and monitor in good working order.

Error beeps generated by the computer are coded in accordance with the BIOS manufacturer. Table 19.2 lists the error-coded beeps produced by AMIBIOS. Others, like Phoenix, have a more elaborate list and produce a combination of beeps to indicate a variety of errors encountered by the POST.

A more reliable and detailed indication of errors is the I/O POST codes. As each POST test is started, a two-digit HEX code is entered into I/O port 0080H which may be displayed by a POST adaptor card slotted into an ISA expansion bus (Fig. 19.2). If the PC fails at any point during the start-up process, the POST code resident in port 0080H represents the failed test. By knowing the full sequence of POST codes generated by the specific BIOS, the displayed code may be used to identify the faulty area.

A more straightforward indication of a fault is an error message displayed on the screen, such as C: DRIVE ERROR or KEYBOARD ERROR.

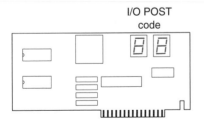

I/O POST code

Figure 19.2 The I/O POST card

Motherboard errors

A large number of errors may be associated with the motherboard, such as faulty CPUs and other support chips, expansion slots and adaptor cards. Before the motherboard is replaced, an attempt should be made to isolate the actual fault which may then be rectified by replacing the faulty card or component only. This may include removing adaptor cards, one at a time, and replacing the CPU and other plug-in components such as the BIOS and keyboard controller chip with known-good units.

On-board options failure

With on-board options such as serial/parallel ports and IDE connector provided by the motherboard, these can be checked by first disabling the option by changing the relevant part of the CMOS set-up. The peripheral may then be installed using the appropriate adaptor card such as an I/O and IDE controller card.

Stage 3 failure – system configuration errors

Configuration errors invariably lead to start-up failure. Some configuration errors such as FDD and HDD types and parameters may be recognised by careful observation of the displayed system configuration as the PC boots up. Errors should be corrected by making the appropriate changes to the CMOS set-up.

Stage 4 failure – no operating system

Following a successful POST indicated by a single beep, a failure to boot up the system by loading the operating system could be caused by several factors: a non-system floppy inserted into drive A: (in which case it should be removed and a reboot attempted), the absence of system files on drive C:, the wrong configuration or wrong cabling of drive C:.

The first action to be taken is to attempt to boot-up the system from drive A: using a known-good system disk. If start-up is successful, drive C: should be checked for hidden system files (IO.SYS and MSDOS.SYS) and the (not hidden) COMMAND.COM. file MS-DOS command DIR C:/A will display all files with their attributes. Missing system files may then be transferred from the system floppy by the command SYS C:. This command usually transfers COMMAND.COM as well. If not, a simple COPY command will suffice.

If the system fails to recognise drive C:, boot-up failure may be caused by an unformatted or unpartitioned hard disk. This can be checked by entering the partitioning procedure using the command FDISK. There must be at least one partition created on the hard disk which must be set ACTIVE for the operating system to be loaded from drive C:. Each partition must be formatted separately. Formatting erases stored data and should not be attempted unless absolutely necessary.

Boot-up failure may also be caused by the incorrect parameter entry of drive C: (master drive) in the CMOS set-up or wrong cabling or loose connections for the power and data/control lines. These should be checked before the hard disk is replaced.

Stage 5 failure – errors in CONFIG.SYS and AUTOEXEC.BAT

Faults in these files do not usually prevent the computer from booting up. Errors are normally indicated on the display. Such errors may be avoided by pressing F8 to bypass both files at the point when MS-DOS begins to be loaded. Alternatively, both files may be single stepped by pressing F5. When rectifying faulty entries, attention should be paid to the loading of device drivers and other TSRs for the most efficient use of installed memory.

Responding to error messages

All error messages and codes should be followed up by first checking relevant cable and adaptor card connections such as the mains and video cables in the case of a blank video screen. In this case the brightness control of the monitor should be checked and the video card examined to ensure that it is properly inserted into the expansion slot.

In the case of a memory error, the SIMMs should be checked to ensure that they are properly seated and the SIMM slots dusted with a soft brush. Before replacing the SIMMs, the memory banks should be emptied, one by one, with the higher numbered banks first, and the system rebooted. The actual faulty SIMMs may thus be isolated and replaced by known-good modules. Before replacing the SIMMs, a check should be made on the speed of the memory chips to ensure compatibility with the clock frequency of the CPU.

Faulty peripherals

Malfunction in a peripheral may be caused by a software or hardware fault. The majority of hardware errors such as wrong cabling or configuration may be picked up during the POST routines. However, a fault in the adaptor/controller card or in the device's electromechanical and control units, such as a disk's Read/Write head or a CD-ROM's speed control circuitry, may only be confirmed by replacing the card or the peripheral with a known-good unit.

Conflict faults (IRQ, base address and DMA) only occur when new peripherals are installed or CMOS set-up or adaptor card configurations are changed. Diagnostic routines including MS-DOS MSD may be used to find the allocation of IRQ, base addresses and DMA channels. Alternatively and more reliably, conflicts may be resolved by removing or disabling the peripherals and their controllers, one at a time. Each time a peripheral is removed, the system should be tested to see if the conflict has been resolved. In this way, the offending peripheral may be identified.

Appendix 1 MS-DOS commands

Command or device driver	Purpose
ANSI.SYS	Defines functions that change display graphics, control cursor movement and reassign keys. This device driver must be loaded by a **device** or **devicehigh** command in your CONFIG.SYS file
append	Enables programs to open data files in specified directories as if the files were in the current directory. Do not use this command when you are running Windows
attrib	Displays or changes file attributes
break	Sets or clears extended Ctrl+C checking. You can use this command at the command prompt or in your CONFIG.SYS file
buffers	Allocates memory for a specified number of disk buffers when your computer starts. You can use this command only in your CONFIG.SYS file
call	Calls one batch program from another without causing the first batch program to stop
cd	Displays the name of the current directory or changes the current directory
chcp	Displays the number of the active character set (code page). You can also use this command to change the active character set for all devices that support character set switching
chdir	See the **cd** command
chkdsk	Checks the status of a disk and displays a status report. Can also fix disk errors. Do not use **chkdsk** with the **/f** switch when you are running Windows
choice	Prompts the user to make a choice in a batch program. Displays a specified prompt and pauses for the user to choose from among a specified set of keys. This command is useful only in batch programs
cls	Clears the screen
command	Starts a new instance of the MS-DOS command interpreter
copy	Copies one or more files to the location you specify
country	Enables MS-DOS to use country-specific conventions for displaying dates, times and currency; for determining the order by which characters are sorted; and for determining which characters can be used in filenames. You can use this command only in your CONFIG.SYS file

Command or device driver	Purpose
ctty	Changes the terminal device used to control your computer
date	Displays the date and prompts you to change the date if necessary
debug	Starts the Debug program, which you can use to test and debug executable files
defrag	Reorganizes the files on a disk to optimize disk performance. Do not use this command when you are running Windows
del (erase)	Deletes the files you specify
deltree	Deletes a directory and all the files and subdirectories that are in it
device	Loads the device driver you specify into memory. You can use this command only in your CONFIG.SYS file
devicehigh	Loads the device driver you specify into upper memory. You can use this command only in your CONFIG.SYS file
dir	Displays a list of the files and subdirectories that are in the directory you specify
diskcomp	Compares the contents of two floppy disks
diskcopy	Copies the entire contents of one floppy disk to another floppy disk
DISPLAY.SYS	Enables you to display international character sets on EGA, VGA and LCD monitors. This device driver must be loaded by a **device** or **devicehigh** command in your CONFIG.SYS file
dos	Specifies that MS-DOS should maintain a link to the upper memory area, load part of itself into the high memory area (HMA), or both. You can use this command only in your CONFIG.SYS file
doskey	Loads the Doskey program into memory. The doskey program recalls MS-DOS commands and enables you to edit command lines and create and run macros
DRIVER.SYS	Creates a logical drive that you can use to refer to a physical floppy disk drive. This device driver must be loaded by a **device** or **devicehigh** command in your CONFIG.SYS file
drivparm	Defines parameters for devices such as disk and tape drives when you start MS-DOS. You can use this command only in your CONFIG.SYS file
echo	Displays or hides the text in batch programs when the program is running. Also indicates whether the command-echoing feature is on or off
edit	Starts MS-DOS Editor, a text editor you can use to create and edit ASCII text files
emm386	Enables or disables EMM386 expanded memory support on a computer with an 80386 or higher processor. Do not use this command when you are running Windows
EMM386.EXE	Provides access to the upper memory area and uses extended memory to simulate expanded memory. This device driver must be loaded by a **device** command in your CONFIG.SYS file and can be used only on computers with an 80386 or higher processor

Command or device driver	Purpose
erase	See the **del** command
exit	Quits the MS-DOS command interpreter (COMMAND.COM) and returns to the program that started the command interpreter, if one exists
expand	Decompresses a compressed file
fasthelp	Displays a list of all MS-DOS commands and gives a brief explanation of each
fastopen	Starts the Fastopen program, which improves performance on computers with large directories. Fastopen decreases the amount of time that MS-DOS takes to open frequently used files. Do not use this command when you are running Windows
fc	Compares two files and displays the differences between them
fcbs	Specifies the number of file control blocks (FCBs) that MS-DOS can have open at the same time. You can use this command only in your CONFIG.SYS file
fdisk	Starts the Fdisk program, which configures a hard disk for use with MS-DOS
files	Specifies the number of files that MS-DOS can access at one time. You can use this command only in your CONFIG.SYS file
find	Searches for a specific string of text in a file or files
for	Runs a specified command for each file in a set of files. You can use this command in batch programs or at the command prompt
format	Formats a disk for use with MS-DOS
goto	Directs MS-DOS to a line in a batch program that is marked by a label you specify. You can use this command only in batch programs
graphics	Loads a program into memory that enables MS-DOS to print the information displayed on your screen. Use the **graphics** command only if you are using a colour or graphics adaptor
help	Starts MS-DOS Help
HIMEM.SYS	Manages the use of extended memory. This device driver must be loaded by a **device** command in your CONFIG.SYS file
if	Performs conditional processing in batch programs. You can use this command only in batch programs
include	Includes the contents of one configuration block within another. You can use this command only in your CONFIG.SYS file
install	Loads a memory-resident program into memory. You can use this command only in your CONFIG.SYS file
interlnk	Starts the Interlink program, which connects two computers by means of parallel or serial ports and enables the computers to share disks and printer ports

Command or device driver	Purpose
INTERLNK.EXE	Redirects commands on Interlnk drives and printer ports to drives and printer ports on the Interlnk server. This device driver must be loaded by a **device** or **devicehigh** command in your CONFIG.SYS file
intersvr	Starts the Interlnk server
keyb	Starts the Keyb program, which configures a keyboard for a specific language
label	Creates, changes or deletes the volume label (name) of a disk
lastdrive	Specifies the maximum number of drives you can access. You can use this command only in your CONFIG.SYS file
lh	See the **loadhigh** command
loadfix	Ensures that a program is loaded above the first 64 kilobytes (KB) of conventional memory
loadhigh (lh)	Loads a program into upper memory
md	Creates a directory or subdirectory
mem	Displays the amount of used and free memory on your computer
memmaker	Starts the MemMaker program, which optimises your computer's memory by configuring device drivers and memory-resident programs to run in the upper memory area. Do not use this command when you are running Windows
menucolor	Sets the text and background colours for the start-up menu. You can use this command only within a menu block in your CONFIG.SYS file
menudefault	Specifies the default menu item on the start-up menu and sets a time-out value if desired. You can use this command only within a menu block in your CONFIG.SYS file
menuitem	Defines up to nine items on a start-up menu. You can use this command only within a menu block in your CONFIG.SYS file
mkdir	See the **md** command
mode	Configures a printer, serial port or display adaptor; sets the typematic rate; redirects printer output from a parallel port to a serial port; prepares, selects, refreshes or displays the numbers of the character sets (code pages) for parallel printers or the keyboard and screen; displays the status of all the devices installed on your computer
more	Displays one screen of output at a time
move	Moves one or more files to the location you specify. Can also be used to rename files and directories
msav	Starts the Microsoft Anti-Virus program, which scans your computer for known viruses
msbackup	Starts the Microsoft Backup program, which backs up or restores one or more files from one disk to another
mscdex	Provides access to CD-ROM drives
msd	Starts the Microsoft Diagnostics program, which provides detailed technical information about your computer

Command or device driver	Purpose
nlsfunc	Starts the Nlsfunc program, which loads country-specific information for national language support (NLS). Do not use this command when you are running Windows
numlock	Specifies whether the Num Lock setting on your numeric keypad is set to ON or OFF. You can use this command only within a menu block in your CONFIG.SYS file
path	Indicates which directories MS-DOS should search for executable files (programs)
pause	Suspends processing of a batch program and displays a message that prompts you to press any key to continue. You can use this command only within batch programs
power	Turns power management on and off, reports the status of power management, and sets levels of power conservation
POWER.EXE	Reduces power consumption when applications and devices are idle. This device driver must be loaded by a **device** or **devicehigh** command in your CONFIG.SYS file
print	Prints a text file
prompt	Changes the appearance of the command prompt
qbasic	Starts MS-DOS QBasic, a program that reads instructions written in the BASIC computer language and interprets them into executable computer code (programs)
RAMDRIVE.SYS	Uses part of your computer's random access memory (RAM) to simulate a hard disk drive. This device driver must be loaded by a **device** or **devicehigh** command in your CONFIG.SYS file
rd	Deletes (removes) a directory
rem	Enables you to include comments (remarks) or prevent commands in a batch program or the CONFIG.SYS file from running
ren	Changes the name of the file or files you specify
rename	See the **ren** command
replace	Replaces files in a destination directory with files in a source directory that have the same name
restore	Restores files that were backed up by using the **backup** command from previous versions of MS-DOS
rmdir	See the **rd** command
scandisk	Checks disks for damage, and repairs them, if needed
set	Displays, sets or removes MS-DOS environment variables. You can use this command in your CONFIG.SYS file in addition to your AUTOEXEC.BAT file or at the command prompt
setver	Displays the version table. Reports a version number to programs or device drivers that were designed for earlier versions of MS-DOS
SETVER.EXE	Loads the MS-DOS version table into memory. This device driver must be loaded by a **device** or **devicehigh** command in your CONFIG.SYS file
share	Starts the Share program, which installs file-sharing and locking capabilities on your disks and network drives

Command or device driver	Purpose
shell	Specifies the name and location of the command interpreter you want MS-DOS to use. You can use this command only in your CONFIG.SYS file
shift	Changes the position of replaceable parameters in a batch program. You can use this command only in batch programs
smartdrv	When specified at the command prompt or in your AUTOEXEC.BAT file, creates a disk cache in extended memory. The cache speeds up access to your hard disk. Do not use this command when you are running Windows
SMARTDRV.EXE	When loaded with a **device** command in your CONFIG.SYS file, this device driver provides compatibility for hard disk controllers that cannot work with EMM386 and Microsoft Windows running in enhanced mode
sort	Reads input, sorts data and writes the results to the screen, a file or another device
stacks	Supports the dynamic use of data stacks to handle hardware interrupts. You can use this command only in your CONFIG.SYS file
submenu	Defines an item on a start-up menu that, when selected, displays another set of choices. You can use this command only within a menu block in your CONFIG.SYS file
subst	Associates a path with a drive letter. Do not use this command when you are running Windows
switches	Specifies special options in MS-DOS. This command can be used only in your CONFIG.SYS file
sys	Create a start-up disk by copying hidden MS-DOS system files and the MS-DOS command interpreter (COMMAND.COM) to the disk
time	Displays the system time or sets your computer's internal clock
tree	Graphically displays the structure of a directory
type	Displays the contents of a text file
undelete	Restores files that were previously deleted by using the **del** command
unformat	Restores a disk that was erased by the **format** command
ver	Displays the MS-DOS version number
verify	Directs MS-DOS to verify that your files are written correctly to a disk, and displays the status of verification. You can use this command either at the command prompt or in your CONFIG.SYS file
vol	Displays the volume label and serial number for a disk, if the disk has them
vsafe	Continuously monitors your computer for viruses and displays a warning when it finds one. Do not use this command when you are running Windows
xcopy	Copies directories, their subdirectories, and files (except hidden and system files)

Source: Material reprinted with permission from Microsoft Corporation.

Appendix 2 Measurement and test instruments

Voltage measurement

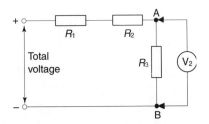

Figure A2.1 Voltage measurements: V_1 for voltage across R_1; V_2 for voltage across R_2

A voltage exists across two points in a circuit. To measure a voltage, a voltmeter is connected across the two points such as A and B in Fig. A2.1. Normally, voltages are measured with respect to the zero voltage or earth line. In this case, one terminal of the voltmeter is connected to earth or the chassis and the other to the test point of which the voltage is required. To reduce the effect of the voltmeter on the circuit, it must have a very large internal resistance compared with the resistance between the two points across which the voltage is to be measured.

Current measurement

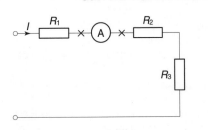

Figure A2.2 Ammeter A measures current I

To measure a current, the circuit is opened at a convenient point and an ammeter is inserted as shown in Fig. A2.2. To ensure minimum interference with the circuit, the ammeter must have a very small internal resistance. Current measurements are not usually employed. Instead, where the value of the current is required, the voltage across a known resistance is measured by a voltmeter, from which the current can then be calculated using Ohm's law, namely $I = V/R$.

Types of measuring instruments

The moving-coil meter is an analogue measuring instrument with an analogue pointer-scale readout. It indicates the average, i.e. d.c., value of the voltage. It may be used for a.c. measurement by rectifying the input before the measurement is made.

The digital voltmeter (DVM) is another analogue measuring instrument with a digital readout. The digital multimeter (DMM) combines the function of a DVM for voltage measurement with that

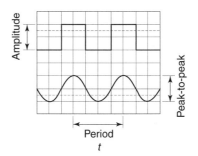

Figure A2.3 Typical dual beam oscilloscope display

of an ammeter and an ohmmeter for current and resistance measurements respectively.

The cathode ray oscilloscope (CRO) is a versatile instrument which displays a.c. waveforms. It may be used to measure the amplitude, the peak-to-peak, the periodic time and hence the frequency of waveforms. In the case of a dual-trace or dual-beam CRO, the phase difference between waveforms may also be measured (Fig. A2.3).

Logic state testing instruments

The logic probe

The logic probe is a logic testing instrument (Fig. A2.4) which investigates the logic state of a node or test point in a digital circuit. It can indicate the presence of a logic 1, logic 0 or an open circuit (o/c) node. Two indicator lamps are used to indicate a HIGH or a LOW. Open circuits or an indeterminate state are indicated by no light while pulses are indicated by a flashing light. A pulse stretching technique is employed by which short duration pulses may be detected by 'stretching' them to ensure that they last long enough for the indicator to be observed by the human eye. Pulses as narrow as 10 ns may be stretched to as much as 50 or 100 ms.

The logic pulser

The logic pulser is used to stimulate logic ICs. It drives an IC pin or node into its opposite logic state, i.e. it drives a LOW node HIGH,

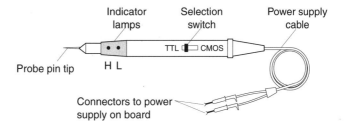

Figure A2.4 The logic probe

and a HIGH node LOW. Together with a logic probe it may be used to verify the function of a gate, a counter or other digital devices. It may also be used to test the continuity of bus lines.

The current tracer

The current tracer is a test instrument which tests the flow of fast-rising current pulses. The tracer senses the magnetic field generated by these pulses and indicates its presence by an indicator such as an LED or a constant tone sound. It may be used with a pulser to identify short circuits to earth or to d.c. supply lines. It may also identify shorts between nodes or lines.

Consider the circuit in Fig. A2.5 in which the input to U_5 is shorted to earth. Initially, the logic probe will indicate a stuck-at-0 condition at the output of U_1 and all along the track feeding the four gates U_2 to U_5. To identify the actual faulty pin, a pulser is used in conjunction with a current tracer. The following procedure is carried out with the d.c. supply switched off. The pulser is placed at any point along the shorted track, say node A. By pulsing this node, a current path is created as shown which ends at the faulty node F. The tracer is then used to follow the current path to its end. The tracer is first placed at node A. The presence of a current is indicated by the tracer by a lighted lamp (or an audible sound). The current tracer is then moved from node A to node B. The tracer indicating lamp remains on. If the tracer is now taken towards node E, the indicating lamp will be off since there is no current pulse between B and E. The tracer is moved towards C maintaining the indication at a constant level. If the tracer is now moved towards G, the indication will once again cease and so on until the tracer reaches node F with nowhere

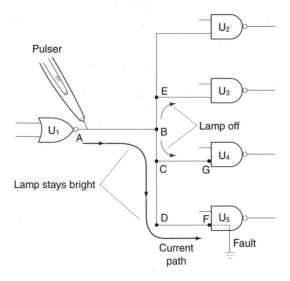

Figure A2.5   The use of current tracer

AQU MEM					STATE LISTING					Set-up:!DEMO DATA

POS	ADDRESS	DATA	SYN	R/W	NMI	IRQ	UNUSED
0000 T	FFFC	E0	0	1	1	1	1111
0001	FFFD	FE	0	1	1	1	1111
0002	FEE0	AE	1	1	1	1	1111
0003	FEE1	03	0	1	1	1	1111
0004	FEE2	F8	0	1	1	1	1111
0005	F803	F8	0	1	1	1	1111
0006	FEE3	D0	1	1	1	1	1111
0007	FEE4	0E	0	1	1	1	1111
0008	FEE5	CA	0	1	1	1	1111
0009	FEF3	A0	1	1	1	1	1111
0010	FEF4	80	0	1	1	1	1111
0011	FEF5	A2	1	1	1	1	1111
0012	FEF6	09	0	1	1	1	1111
0013	FEF7	94	1	1	1	1	1111
0014	FEF8	0E	0	1	1	1	1111
0015	000E	80	0	1	1	1	1111

RUN STATUS

SINGLE MODE		STOPPED		TRIGGERED

Inputs :	C883	00	0	1	1	1	1101

SINGLE	REPEAT	MONITOR	COND RPT.	FAST ROLL	SLOW ROLL	INFO	EXIT

Figure A2.6   Logic analyser display – data domain

else to go. In general the tracer is moved around the circuit along a path that keeps the indicating lamp (or sound) constant until the faulty node is found.

Similar procedures may be followed for a solder bridge fault and other faults such as V_{CC} to ground faults.

The logic clip

The logic clip (Fig. A2.6) is another device that can indicate the logic state of an IC pin. In this case the IC clip reads the logic states of all pins simultaneously. The state of each pin is indicated by an LED: ON for logic 1 and OFF for logic 0. A pulse is indicated by a dimmed light.

The logic clip may be used to verify the truth table of an IC and to test a counter or a shift register for faults on outputs, resets, clears or other pins.

The logic comparator

The logic comparator compares the logic state of an IC pin with the logic state produced by a known-good IC. It repeats this test for all the pins and displays any errors in performance pin by pin. It carries out this test while the suspected IC remains in circuit (in-circuit test) very quickly and efficiently. The disadvantage of this type of logic state tester is the fact that a known-good IC must be available.

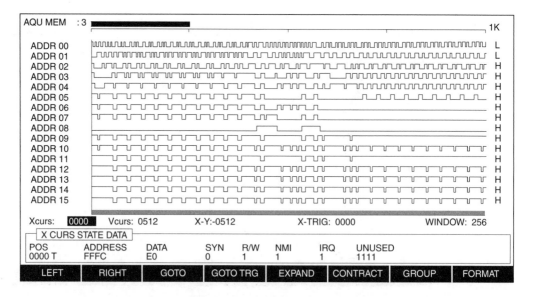

Figure A2.7 Logic analyser display – time domain

The logic analyser

Logic state testing instruments such as the logic probe are extremely limited when testing a microprocessor-based bus-structured system. In a bus-structured system, the logic level of an individual bus line does not provide enough information about the operation of the system. For this, it is necessary to look at the logic levels of all lines on the bus simultaneously. In this way a complete address or data may be ascertained. Furthermore, one single word on a bus does not provide adequate test information about the system. What is required is the sequence of words or events that appear on the bus, e.g. a sequence of addresses or data or both. The logic analyser provides such information. It has a number of inputs known as channels (e.g. 32, 48 or more). These channels, which are connected to appropriate bus lines, have their logic levels monitored and captured simultaneously and stored in the RAM of the logic analyser. They may then be displayed in the form of a sequence of data (data domain, Fig. A2.6) or a set of waveforms (time domain, (Fig. A2.7)).

The signature analyser

The signature analyser captures a stream of logic pulses on a bus line. The series of pulses are reduced to a 16-bit residue known as the signature by the use of a cyclic redundancy count (CRC). The signature is unique to the particular sequence of pulse stream to an accuracy of 99.98 per cent. The 16-bit signature is then converted into a four-digit HEX number.

Signature analysis using the CRC technique is widely used for testing memory devices as well as complete systems. The process involves writing a program which will test various parts of the system including the CPU and memory chips. The system is then stimulated with a test program and a signature analyser is used to test for correct signatures at predetermined test nodes. The test program itself may be stored in a ROM device within the system or it may be fed externally by a peripheral device or by the signature analyser itself. The signature at each node is then monitored and compared with that produced by a known-good system. The correct signatures may be stored in a ROM device to make comparison quick and easy.

Testing a CPU involves going through some or all of its instructions and checking the response. Testing a ROM involves reading the contents of memory locations and using CRC to produce a signature which is then compared with that produced by a known-good ROM. Testing a RAM device involves writing ones, zeros or alternate ones and zeros (the checkerboard test pattern) into each location, reading the contents and noting the signature thus produced.

Signatures generated by a unit under test may then be compared with those generated by a known-good unit to ascertain faulty conditions.

Appendix 3   Binary and hexadecimal

The binary system uses two discrete levels: a logic 0 and a logic 1. A single binary digit, known as a bit, provides basic 'YES' or 'NO' information. More information may be conveyed by grouping a number of bits together, e.g. 4, 8, 16. Such groupings are known as words. A word is a group of binary digits or bits which form the basic unit of information in a digital system. A 4-bit word, known as a nibble, can be used to represent $2^4 = 16$ different numbers from 0 to 15. An 8-bit word, known as a byte, can represent $2^8 = 256$ different numbers from 0 to 255 and so on.

In the same way as denary (decimal) columns represent increasing powers of 10, binary columns represent increasing powers of 2 with the rightmost bit known as the least significant bit, having a value of $2^0 = 1$. The next column has a value of $2^1 = 2$, the third $2^2 = 4$ and so on as shown in Table A3.1. In any binary word, the rightmost bit is known as the least significant bit (LSB) and the leftmost bit is known as the most significant bit (MSB).

Table A3.1

Decimal	Binary columns		
	C (4)	B (2)	A (1)
0	0	0	0
1	0	0	1
2	0	1	0
3	0	1	1
4	1	0	0
5	1	0	1
6	1	1	0
7	1	1	1

Hexadecimal

In order to avoid the use of long strings of binary digits, hexadecimal notation is used. Hexadecimal numbers have a base of 16 and hence have 16 distinct symbols:

0, 1, 2, 3, 4, 5, 6, 7, 8, 9, A, B, C, D, E, F

with A, B, C, D, E and F representing denary numbers 10, 11, 12, 13, 14 and 15 respectively. Each 4-bit binary number may thus be represented by a single hexadecimal digit as shown in Table A3.2. An 8-bit binary number is represented by a two-digit hexadecimal number as shown in Fig. A3.1. To avoid confusion, the base (2 for binary and 16 for hexadecimal) may be shown as a subscript, e.g. 1001_2 and $A3_{16}$. A more common way of distinguishing between the two types of numbering systems is to terminate binary numbers with a 'B' and hexadecimal numbers with an 'H'. For instance, binary 0110 is written as 0110B and hexadecimal number 2F as 2FH.

Table A3.2

Hexadecimal	Binary
0	0000
1	0001
2	0010
3	0011
4	0100
5	0101
6	0110
7	0111
8	1000
9	1001
A	1010
B	1011
C	1100
D	1101
E	1110
F	1111

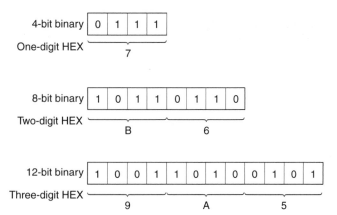

Figure A3.1

Appendix 4 Chip markings

A4.1 Processors

Intel

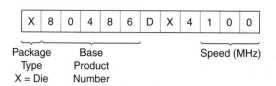

Package Type X = Die	Base Product Number	Speed (MHz)

Intel Pentium

Top Markings

B-Step Production Units – Top:

KB8Ø521EXZZZ SYYYY 256K

XXXXX XXXXX XXXXX XXXXX XXXXX
XXXXX XXXXX XXXXX XXXXX XXXXX

int**el**®

XXXXX XXXXX XXXXX XXXXX XXXXX
XXXXX XXXXX XXXXX XXXXX XXXXX

FFFFFFFF-XXXX

INTEL Ⓜ Ⓒ '94 '95

Bottom Markings

B-, C-, and sA-Step Production Units – Bottom:

XXXXXXXXAA
YYYYYYYYAA
MALAY K

KB8Ø521EXZZZ
SYYYY LLLK

Notes:
- ZZZ = Speed (MHz)
- QYYYY = Sample Specification Number.
- SYYYY = S-spec Number.

- FFFFFFFF = FPO # (Test Lot Traceability #)

IBM

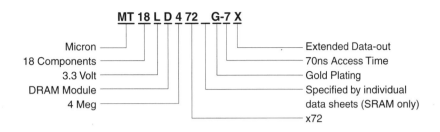

Micron
18 Components
3.3 Volt
DRAM Module
4 Meg
x72
Extended Data-out
70ns Access Time
Gold Plating
Specified by individual
data sheets (SRAM only)

IBM

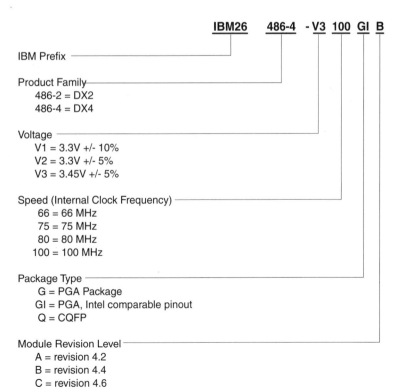

IBM Prefix

Product Family
    486-2 = DX2
    486-4 = DX4

Voltage
    V1 = 3.3V +/- 10%
    V2 = 3.3V +/- 5%
    V3 = 3.45V +/- 5%

Speed (Internal Clock Frequency)
    66 = 66 MHz
    75 = 75 MHz
    80 = 80 MHz
    100 = 100 MHz

Package Type
    G = PGA Package
    GI = PGA, Intel comparable pinout
    Q = CQFP

Module Revision Level
    A = revision 4.2
    B = revision 4.4
    C = revision 4.6

Cyrix

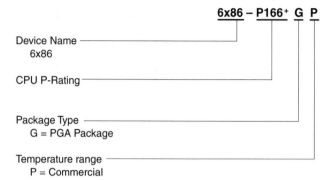

6x86 – P166⁺ G P

Device Name
6x86

CPU P-Rating

Package Type
G = PGA Package

Temperature range
P = Commercial

AMD

AMD ₖ 86 Processor Data Sheet

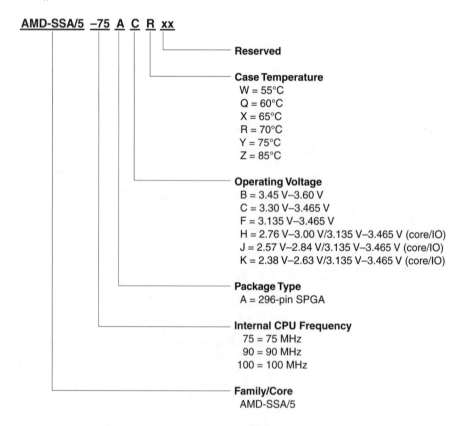

AMD-SSA/5 –75 A C R xx

Reserved

Case Temperature
W = 55°C
Q = 60°C
X = 65°C
R = 70°C
Y = 75°C
Z = 85°C

Operating Voltage
B = 3.45 V–3.60 V
C = 3.30 V–3.465 V
F = 3.135 V–3.465 V
H = 2.76 V–3.00 V/3.135 V–3.465 V (core/IO)
J = 2.57 V–2.84 V/3.135 V–3.465 V (core/IO)
K = 2.38 V–2.63 V/3.135 V–3.465 V (core/IO)

Package Type
A = 296-pin SPGA

Internal CPU Frequency
75 = 75 MHz
90 = 90 MHz
100 = 100 MHz

Family/Core
AMD-SSA/5

AMD486

AMD486

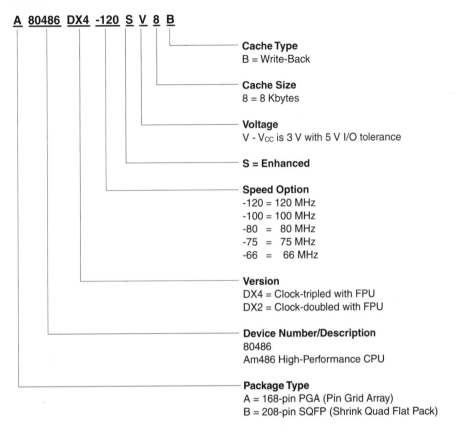

A 80486 DX4 -120 S V 8 B

Cache Type
B = Write-Back

Cache Size
8 = 8 Kbytes

Voltage
V - V_{CC} is 3 V with 5 V I/O tolerance

S = Enhanced

Speed Option
-120 = 120 MHz
-100 = 100 MHz
-80 = 80 MHz
-75 = 75 MHz
-66 = 66 MHz

Version
DX4 = Clock-tripled with FPU
DX2 = Clock-doubled with FPU

Device Number/Description
80486
Am486 High-Performance CPU

Package Type
A = 168-pin PGA (Pin Grid Array)
B = 208-pin SQFP (Shrink Quad Flat Pack)

A4.2 Memory chips

Micron

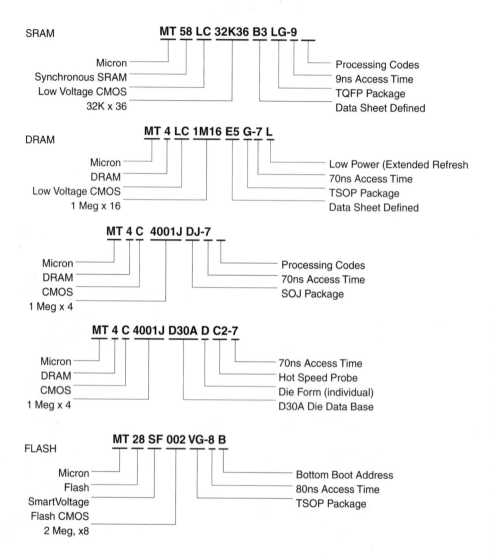

SRAM

MT 58 LC 32K36 B3 LG-9

Micron
Synchronous SRAM
Low Voltage CMOS
32K x 36

Processing Codes
9ns Access Time
TQFP Package
Data Sheet Defined

DRAM

MT 4 LC 1M16 E5 G-7 L

Micron
DRAM
Low Voltage CMOS
1 Meg x 16

Low Power (Extended Refresh
70ns Access Time
TSOP Package
Data Sheet Defined

MT 4 C 4001J DJ-7

Micron
DRAM
CMOS
1 Meg x 4

Processing Codes
70ns Access Time
SOJ Package

MT 4 C 4001J D30A D C2-7

Micron
DRAM
CMOS
1 Meg x 4

70ns Access Time
Hot Speed Probe
Die Form (individual)
D30A Die Data Base

FLASH

MT 28 SF 002 VG-8 B

Micron
Flash
SmartVoltage
Flash CMOS
2 Meg, x8

Bottom Boot Address
80ns Access Time
TSOP Package

A4.3 Memory modules

Micron

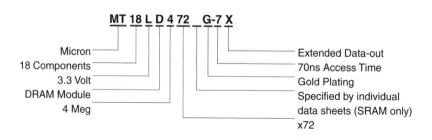

MT 18 L D 4 72 G-7 X

Micron
18 Components
3.3 Volt
DRAM Module
4 Meg

Extended Data-out
70ns Access Time
Gold Plating
Specified by individual
data sheets (SRAM only)
x72

IBM

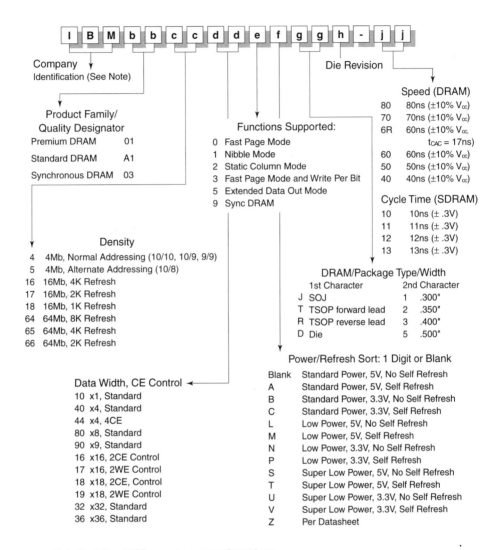

IBMbbccddeffgghh-jj

Company
Identification (See Note)

Die Revision

Product Family/
Quality Designator
Premium DRAM   01
Standard DRAM   A1
Synchronous DRAM   03

Functions Supported:
0 Fast Page Mode
1 Nibble Mode
2 Static Column Mode
3 Fast Page Mode and Write Per Bit
5 Extended Data Out Mode
9 Sync DRAM

Speed (DRAM)
80   80ns (±10% V_{cc})
70   70ns (±10% V_{cc})
6R   60ns (±10% V_{cc}, t_{CAC} = 17ns)
60   60ns (±10% V_{cc})
50   50ns (±10% V_{cc})
40   40ns (±10% V_{cc})

Cycle Time (SDRAM)
10   10ns (± .3V)
11   11ns (± .3V)
12   12ns (± .3V)
13   13ns (± .3V)

Density
4   4Mb, Normal Addressing (10/10, 10/9, 9/9)
5   4Mb, Alternate Addressing (10/8)
16   16Mb, 4K Refresh
17   16Mb, 2K Refresh
18   16Mb, 1K Refresh
64   64Mb, 8K Refresh
65   64Mb, 4K Refresh
66   64Mb, 2K Refresh

DRAM/Package Type/Width

1st Character		2nd Character	
J	SOJ	1	.300"
T	TSOP forward lead	2	.350"
R	TSOP reverse lead	3	.400"
D	Die	5	.500"

Power/Refresh Sort: 1 Digit or Blank

Blank	Standard Power, 5V, No Self Refresh
A	Standard Power, 5V, Self Refresh
B	Standard Power, 3.3V, No Self Refresh
C	Standard Power, 3.3V, Self Refresh
L	Low Power, 5V, No Self Refresh
M	Low Power, 5V, Self Refresh
N	Low Power, 3.3V, No Self Refresh
P	Low Power, 3.3V, Self Refresh
S	Super Low Power, 5V, No Self Refresh
T	Super Low Power, 5V, Self Refresh
U	Super Low Power, 3.3V, No Self Refresh
V	Super Low Power, 3.3V, Self Refresh
Z	Per Datasheet

Data Width, CE Control
10   x1, Standard
40   x4, Standard
44   x4, 4CE
80   x8, Standard
90   x9, Standard
16   x16, 2CE Control
17   x16, 2WE Control
18   x18, 2CE, Control
19   x18, 2WE Control
32   x32, Standard
36   x36, Standard

Note: The letters "IBM" may not appear on the package.

Appendix 5 Logic devices

Logic gates A logic gate is a two-state device, i.e. it has a two-state output: an output of 0 volts representing logic 0 (or LOW) and a fixed voltage output representing logic 1 (or HIGH). The logic gate may have several inputs, all of which may be in one of the two possible logic states: 0 or 1. Logic gates may be used to perform several functions, e.g. AND, OR, NAND or NOR.

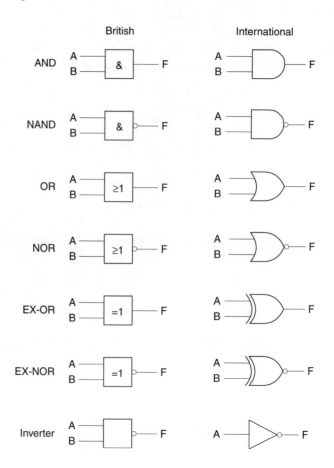

Figure A5.1

Table A5.1

Inputs				Output functions			
A	B	AND	NAND	OR	NOR	EX-OR	EX-NOR
0	0	0	1	0	1	0	1
0	1	0	1	1	0	1	0
1	0	0	1	1	0	1	0
1	1	1	0	1	0	0	1

The list of all possible combinations of the input and their respective outputs is known as the truth table of the gate. Fig. A5.1 shows the British and international standard symbols and Table A5.1 shows their truth table.

Logic packages

Logic elements including gates and memory devices are manufactured in IC packages. These ICs are classified into categories, known as families, according to the number of gates or equivalent elements that they contain. These families are:

Small scale integration (SSI): up to 10 gates
Medium scale integration (MSI): 10–100 gates
Large scale integration (LSI): 100–1000 gates
Very large scale integration (VLSI): 1000–10,1000 gates
Super large scale integration (SLSI): 10,000–100,000 gates

The level of integration represents the complexity of the IC package. It increases in powers of 10, i.e. 10, 100, 1000 and so on. Small and medium scale integration (SSI and MSI) provide discrete logic elements such as gates, counters and registers. Large and very large scale integration (LSI and VLSI) provide memory chips, microprocessors and complete systems such as 4-bit microcomputers.

Fig. A5.2 shows a number of logic gate IC packages.

Other logic devices

Other logic devices that are commonly used in computers are shown in Fig. A5.3

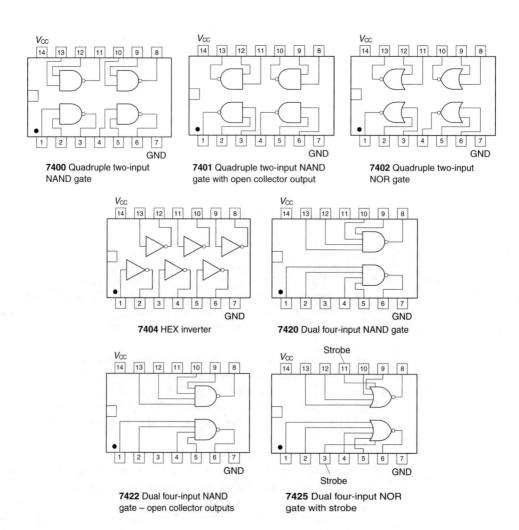

7400 Quadruple two-input NAND gate

7401 Quadruple two-input NAND gate with open collector output

7402 Quadruple two-input NOR gate

7404 HEX inverter

7420 Dual four-input NAND gate

7422 Dual four-input NAND gate – open collector outputs

7425 Dual four-input NOR gate with strobe

Figure A5.2

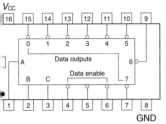

74137 Three- to eight-line decoder/
demultiplexer with address latches

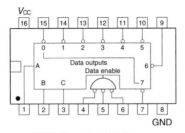

74138 Three- to eight-line
decoder/multiplexer

74238 Three- to eight-line decoder/multiplexer

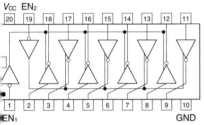

74240 Octal buffer – three-state
inverting

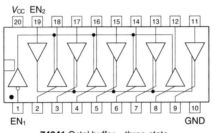

74241 Octal buffer – three-state
non-inverting

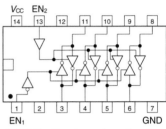

74242 Quad bus transceiver – inverting

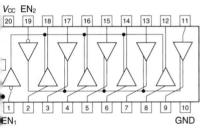

74244 Octal buffer – three-state
non-inverting

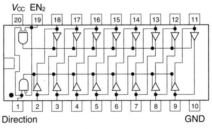

74245 Octal bus transceiver with
three-state outputs

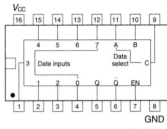

74251 One of eight data selector/multiplexer
with three-state outputs

Figure A5.3

Appendix 6 Revision questions and answers

The following questions are multiple choice. Choose an answer from (a) to (d) for each question and then check your results against the answers given on p. 232.

answers given on p. 232.

Revision questions: intermediate level

1. Read only memory (ROM) is defined as
    a. volatile memory
    b. read/write memory
    c. temporary memory
    d. permanent memory

2. The power supply unit of a PC produces the following voltages
    a. +5 V only
    b. +5 V and −5 V only
    c. +5 V, −5 V and +12 V only
    d. +5 V, −5 V, +12 V and −12 V only

3. A typical fuse rating for a PC power unit is
    a. 0.5 A
    b. 1.0 A
    c. 3.0 A
    d. 13 A

4. A PC normally supports
    a. up to four serial ports
    b. up to two serial ports
    c. parallel ports only
    d. one serial port only

5. A processor with 20 address lines can directly address
    a. 0.5MB of memory
    b. 640KB of memory
    c. 1MB of memory
    d. 16MB of memory

6. Which one of the following elements of the motherboard provides control and synchronisation of the system?

   a. Processor
   b. ROM
   c. RAM
   d. Interrupt controller

7. Which one of the following provides fast memory transfer?

   a. DMA controller
   b. Coprocessor
   c. Input/output adaptor
   d. Disk controller

8. Computer system memory comprises

   a. ROM devices
   b. RAM devices
   c. disk drives
   d. video memory devices

9. DRAM devices have a typical speed of

   a. 20 ns
   b. 20 ms
   c. 60 ns
   d. 60 ms

10. A processor with the following markings

    X80486DX2-100

    has an internal speed of

    a. 50 MHz
    b. 100 MHz
    c. 150 MHz
    d. 200 MHz

11. One of the functions of BIOS is to

    a. carry out power on self-test (POST)
    b. reset the CPU
    c. upgrade system memory
    d. provide overcurrent protection

12. Which of the following types of connectors is commonly used for a parallel printer interface?

    a. 14-pin DIN
    b. 36-way Centronics
    c. 15-way D-type
    d. 50-way edge connector

13. In serial communications

    a. data bits are sent simultaneously
    b. data bits are sent one at time
    c. a video interface is used
    d. colour-coded signals are transmitted

14. IDE hard disk drives employ a

    a. 34-way cable
    b. 40-way cable
    c. 50-way cable
    d. 34-way control and 20-way data cables

15. A 3½ inch floppy disk has a capacity of

    a. 360KB
    b. 720MB
    c. 1.44KB
    d. 1.44MB

16. Which of the following video monitors can display the largest number of colours?

    a. Monochrome
    b. TTL RGB
    c. Analogue RGB
    d. Composite video

17. Which of the following computer ports are used for VGA video display?

    a. 9-way male D-type
    b. 9-way female D-type
    c. 15-way male D-type
    d. 15-way female D-type

18. A computer will fail to boot up if

    a. IO.SYS is missing
    b. CONFIG.SYS is missing
    c. AUTOEXEC.BAT is missing
    d. the mouse is not connected

19. Following a successful POST routine,

    a. no beeps are produced
    b. a single beep is produced
    c. a continuous beep is produced
    d. two successive beeps are produced

20. It is necessary to use a DVM to measure the output voltages of a power supply. Which one of the following voltage ranges should be selected?

    a. 5 V a.c.   b. 30 V a.c.
    c. 5 V d.c.   d. 30 V d.c.

21. Which one of the following semiconductor packages is most commonly used for general purpose computer chips?

    a. CMOS   b. TTL
    c. EPROM   d. NMOS

22. Which one of the following functions is carried out by BIOS during the power-up process?

    a. Check the presence of an application program
    b. Partition the hard disk
    c. Simple RAM and ROM test
    d. Pass control to the application program

23. MS-DOS is

    a. a microprocessor
    b. an application program
    c. a microcomputer
    d. an operating system

24. A computer-aided design (CAD) package requires high quality video display. Which one of the following is most appropriate?

    a. 40 × 25 text mode
    b. 80 × 25 text mode
    c. 640 × 350 pixels, VGA
    d. 1024 × 768 pixels, SVGA

25. A cathode ray tube is used in an oscilloscope to display

    a. machine code programs
    b. memory addresses in binary form
    c. memory addresses in HEX form
    d. time-related waveforms

26. A logic probe is used to

    a. indicate the logic state of a test node
    b. display waveforms of serial signals
    c. test the resistance of a conducting track
    d. indicate the presence of system files

27. An application program is generally constructed to run on a specific

    a. computer
    b. operating system
    c. storage system
    d. make of hard disk drive

28. DOS command DIR is used to

    a. redirect the output from serial to parallel
    b. change the working drive
    c. list the files in a directory
    d. configure a new device

29. Which one of the following devices requires a 40-way ribbon cable?

    a. SCSI hard disk drive
    b. SCSI CD-ROM drive
    c. IDE hard disk drive
    d. ST506 hard disk drive

30. The normal logic High voltage range for a TTL device is

    a. 0 V to 2.5 V
    b. 2.5 V to 3.5 V
    c. 3.5 V to 5.25 V
    d. 5.25 V to 15 V

Revision questions: advanced level

1. Compared with TTL, a CMOS device
    a. has greater power dissipation
    b. has smaller power dissipation
    c. uses bipolar transistors
    d. is faster

2. Which of the following represents a clock waveform?

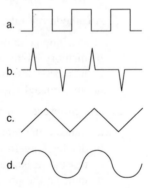

    a.
    b.
    c.
    d.

3. The smallest active element of a video display is called
    a. a bit
    b. a nibble
    c. a byte
    d. a pixel

4. Which one of the following processors has a potentially faster clock?
    a. 80286
    b. 80386
    c. 80486
    d. Pentium

5. The power good (PG) signal of a power supply unit in a computer system has a voltage of

 a. +5 V   b. −5 V
 c. +12 V   d. −12 V

6. Refer to Fig. A6.2. The function of memory area marked X is for

 a. system RAM
 b. video display
 c. BIOS data
 d. application programs

7. Memory address FFFF:0004 represents absolute address

 a. 10003H
 b. 4FFFFH
 c. FFFF4H
 d. FF4FFH

8. The high memory area (HMA) is

 a. all memory space above 1MB
 b. all memory space above 640KB
 c. all memory space below 640 KB
 d. a 64KB segment immediately above 1MB

9. A memory chip with the following markings
 MT4C1M16E5TG-7 L
 is a

 a. 7 ns SRAM chip
 b. 70 ns SRAM chip
 c. 7 ns DRAM chip
 d. 70 ns DRAM chip

10. The purpose of cache memory is

 a. to provide wait states for the CPU
 b. to provide extra memory
 c. to speed up the operation of CPU
 d. to provide back-up memory

11. In order for the CPU to be able to address memory above 1 MB, the following must be included in CONFIG.SYS:

 a. DEVICE=C:\DOS\EMM386.EXE
 b. DEVICE=C:\DOS\HIMEM.SYS
 c. DEVICE=C:\MOUSE\MOUSE.SYS
 d. DEVICE=C:\DOS\COUNTRY.SYS

12. CONFIG.SYS and AUTOEXEC.BAT files may be bypassed during the boot-up stage by pressing

 a. F3
 b. F5
 c. F8
 d. DEL

Figure A6.2

13. Refer to Fig. A6.3. The block labelled 8042 is the

    a. system BIOS chip
    b. keyboard controller chip
    c. memory chip
    d. CMOS chip

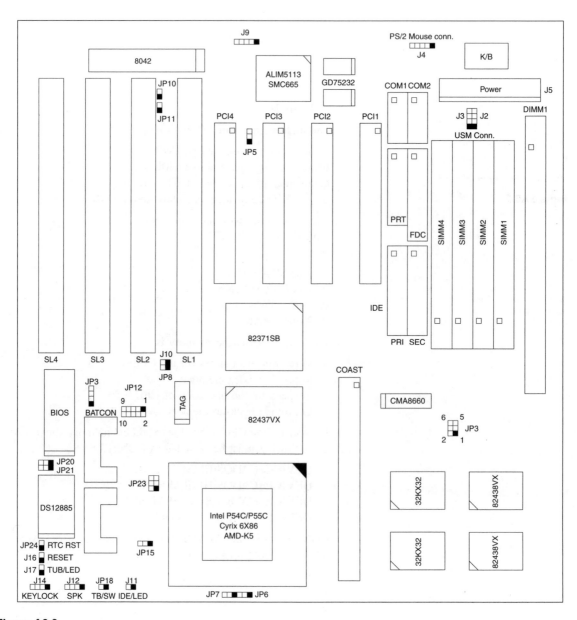

Figure A6.3

14. Refer to Fig. A6.3. The motherboard shown supports

   a. two ISA and four PCI expansion slots
   b. four ISA and four PCI expansion slots
   c. four ISA and four VESA expansion slots
   d. four 16-bit ISA and four 8-bit ISA expansion slots

15. Refer to Fig. A6.3. Which of the following will contain the system memory?

   a. SL1–SL4
   b. PCI1– PCI4
   c. 82371SB and 82437VX
   d. SIMM1–SIMM4

16. Refer to Fig. A6.3. DIMM1 is not used for

   a. cache memory
   b. extended memory
   c. expanded memory
   d. system memory

17. Refer to Fig. A6.3. The blocks labelled PRI and SEC are provided for

   a. IDE drives
   b. floppy disk drives
   c. parallel ports
   d. primary and secondary storage

18. Which of the following IRQs is allocated for COM1?

   a. IRQ2
   b. IRQ3
   c. IRQ4
   d. IRQ5

19. Which of the following port addresses are normally allocated to COM1 and COM2?

	COM1	COM2
a.	03F8H	02F8H
b.	02F8H	03F8H
c.	03F8H	03E8H
d.	03E8H	`02E8H

20. The purpose of incorporating a line driver within an RS-232 interface is to

   a. convert serial data into parallel data
   b. provide error detection
   c. provide TTL to RS-232 voltage shifting
   d. provide a synchronising clock pulse

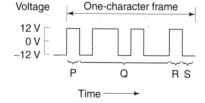

Figure A6.4

21. Refer to Fig. A6.4. The bit marked R is the

   a. start bit   b. stop bit
   c. parity bit   d. clock bit

22. In asynchronous serial transmission, logic 1 is represented by a voltage between

    a. +3 V and −3 V
    b. +5 V and +15 V
    c. −5 V and −15 V
    d. + 5 V and −5 V

23. MS DOS's INTERLNK.EXE provides communication between a computer and

    a. a printer
    b. a scanner
    c. a modem
    d. another computer

24. The MODE command may be used to

    a. configure serial ports
    b. change the working directory
    c. redirect a modem output
    d. change the operating mode of the computer

25. A hard disk with 685 cylinders, 16 heads and 38 sectors per track has a capacity of

    a. 3.9MB
    b. 203MB
    c. 213MB
    d. 1.9GB

26. LBA is enabled if

    a. the system memory exceeds 1MB
    b. the HD capacity exceeds 0.5GB
    c. the system files are missing
    d. more than eight ISA slots are used

27. In a SCSI bus, the host adaptor ID is normally set to

    a. 00
    b. 01
    c. 10
    d. 07

28. The resolution of a video monitor is given as 640 × 480. The total number of pixels is

    a. 640
    b. 480
    c. 1120
    d. 307,200

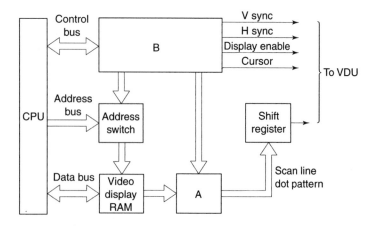

Figure A6.5

29. In a text mode video display, each character is allocated

    a. 1 byte of memory
    b. 2 bytes of memory
    c. 4 bytes of memory
    d. 8 bytes of memory

30. An all-point addressable (APA) video display with a resolution of 1024 × 768 and a colour depth of 16 bits requires a video memory of

    a. 512KB
    b. 1MB
    c. 2MB
    d. 4MB

31. Refer to Fig. A6.5. Block A is the

    a. DMA controller
    b. character generator
    c. interrupt controller
    d. CRT controller

32. Refer to Fig. A6.5. Block B is the

    a. DMA controller
    b. character generator
    c. UART
    d. CRT controller

33. A null-modem cable has

    a. TD and RD lines crossed
    b. CD and DTR crossed
    c. RTS and CTS only crossed
    d. no lines crossed

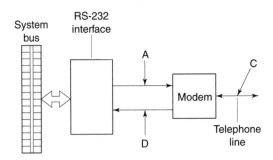

Figure A6.6

34. Refer to Fig. A6.6. The signal at A comprises

    a. outgoing serial data at RS-232 voltage levels
    b. outgoing serial data at TTL voltage levels
    c. a sound modulated tone
    d. a video modulated signal

35. System memory up to 640KB is known as

    a. extended memory
    b. upper memory
    c. expanded memory
    d. conventional memory

36. Which one of the following is NOT a function of an internal speaker of a personal computer?

    a. Generates audible beeps
    b. Signals error conditions
    c. Picks up external sounds
    d. Produces sound effects

37. A modem using four-phase QPSK with a baud rate of 1200 has a transfer rate of

    a. 300 bits per second
    b. 1200 bits per second
    c. 2400 bits per second
    d. 4800 bits per second

38. Compared with a hard disk drive, the CD-ROM drive

    a. has a variable rotation speed
    b. has a faster data transfer rate
    c. requires a SCSI
    d. has multiple heads

39. MSCDEX.EXE provides access to a

    a. hard drive
    b. floppy drive
    c. CD-ROM drive
    d. system memory

40. Sound cards use a standard sampling rate of

    a. 20 kHz
    b. 40 kHz
    c. 44.1 kHz
    d. 100 kHz

41. An 8-bit analogue-to-digital converter provides

    a. 8 different levels
    b. 16 different levels
    c. 80 different levels
    d. 256 different levels

42. A loopback block is used to

    a. test a serial port
    b. test a mouse
    c. test a video port
    d. test expansion slots

43. A break-out-box is used to test

    a. a video monitor
    b. an expansion bus
    c. a parallel cable
    d. a serial cable

44. Which one of the following interfaces is most likely to be used for a keyboard?

    a. Serial synchronous
    b. Parallel synchronous
    c. Serial asynchronous
    d. Parallel asynchronous

45. Compared with a logic probe, the oscilloscope

    a. can detect noise signals
    b. can detect tristate conditions
    c. is simple to use
    d. is cheap in price

46. A programmable peripheral interface is programmed by

    a. control signals from the peripheral
    b. setting appropriate pins HIGH
    c. resetting the device
    d. software commands from the CPU

47. The function of the system lock on a computer system is to

    a. disable the system memory
    b. disable the keyboard
    c. disconnect the mains from the system
    d. disable the power supply

48. The purpose of a matrix in a keyboard is to

    a. allow instantaneous detection of a pressed key
    b. increase the number of keys
    c. allow more than one key to be pressed at the same time
    d. allow different keyboard configurations

49. An RS-232 communication system employs simultaneous reception and transmission using X-ON/X-OFF. The system may be described as

    a. half duplex with software flow control
    b. full duplex with software flow control
    c. half duplex without software flow control
    d. half duplex without flow control

50. EMM386.EXE is required in order to

    a. access upper memory
    b. access expanded memory
    c. access extended memory
    d. install the operating system

51. Refer to Fig. A6.7. Which one of the following is correct?

    a. The computer is the DTE, the modem is the DCE
    b. The computer is the DCE, the modem is the DTE
    c. Both are DTEs
    d. Both are DCEs

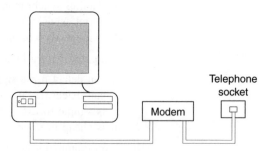

Figure A6.7

52. The Xmodem CRC protocol uses

    a. no ASCII formatted data
    b. only ASCII formatted data
    c. a block size of 128 bytes
    d. no error detection

53. The function of CONFIG.SYS is to

    a. load and execute appropriate device drivers
    b. pass control to the user
    c. perform diagnostic routines
    d. bypass the operating system

54. The MODE command may be used to

    a. set the number of serial ports
    b. set the number of parallel ports
    c. direct the output from the parallel port to the serial port
    d. set the last drive

55. A 4MB system memory which is directly addressable by a processor is known as

    a. conventional memory
    b. extended memory
    c. expanded memory
    d. video memory

56. Refer to Fig. A6.8. Which one of the following is the correct grid notation of the arrowed pin?

    a. A1
    b. A17
    c. S1
    d. S17

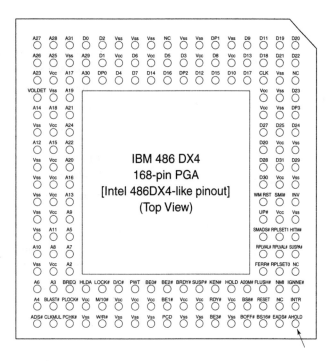

Figure A6.8

57. Hidden files may be displayed by

    a. DIR
    b. DIR/a
    c. DIR\a
    d. DIR/p

58. POST (power-on self test) routines are contained in the

    a. CMOS set-up chip
    b. memory RAM
    c. ROM BIOS
    d. hard disk

59. Which of the following files are necessary to boot up a computer?

    a. CONFIG.SYS
    b. AUTOEXEC.BAT
    c. EMM386.EXE
    d. IO.SYS.

60. A null-modem connects

    a. two computers
    b. two modems
    c. a modem and a computer
    d. a modem and a telephone receiver

61. The purpose of a CRT controller is to

    a. provide video storage
    b. set the EHT voltage of the monitor
    c. store different character fonts
    d. control and synchronise video generation

62. The BIOS data is stored within 16 bytes of system memory commencing at

    a. AAAA:0000
    b. 0000:AAAA
    c. FFFF:0000
    d. 0000:FFFF

63. The purpose of multiplexing address and data buses is to

    a. increase memory access speed
    b. reduce memory access speed
    c. increase the number of pins on the processor
    d. reduce the number of pins on the processor

64. Refer to Fig. A6.9 which shows the top view of a 68-pin chip. Which one of the following corresponds to pin 17?

    a. A
    b. B
    c. C
    d. D

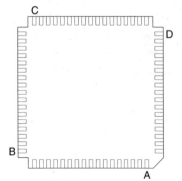

Figure A6.9

65. A computer has the following memory components:

SIMMs   4MB
L1 cache   256KB
L2 cache   512KB

The total system memory is

a. 4MB
b. 4.25MB
c. 4.5MB
d. 4.75MB

Answers to intermediate level

1. d	11. a	21 d
2. d	12. b	22. c
3. c	13. b	23. d
4. a	14. b	24. d
5. c	15. d	25. d
6. a	16. c	26. a
7. a	17. d	27. b
8. b	18. a	28. c
9. c	19. b	29. c
10. b	20. d	30. c

Answers to advanced level

1. b	23. d	45. a
2. a	24. a	46. d
3. d	25. b	47. b
4. d	26. b	48. a
5. a	27. d	49. b
6. b	28. d	50. a
7. c	29. b	51. a
8. d	30. c	52. c
9. d	31. b	53. a
10. c	32. d	54. c
11. b	33. a	55. b
12. c	34. a	56. b
13. b	35. d	57. b
14. b	36. c	58. c
15. d	37. c	59. d
16. d	38. a	60. a
17. a	39. c	61. d
18. c	40. c	62. c
19. a	41. d	63. d
20. c	42. a	64. d
21. c	43. d	65. a
22. c	44. a	

Index